Automation

Its anatomy and physiology

___

CONTEMPORARY
SCIENCE
PAPERBACKS
8

To my wife
FAY

'When a true genius appears in the world, you may know him by this sign that the dunces are all in confederacy against him.'

JONATHAN SWIFT

J. ROSE M.SC., PH.D., F.R.I.C., F.I.L., M.B.I.M.
Principal, Blackburn College of Technology and Design

Automation

Its anatomy and physiology

OLIVER & BOYD
EDINBURGH AND LONDON

303.4
R796a
1967

OLIVER AND BOYD LTD
Tweeddale Court Edinburgh 1
39a Welbeck Street London W.1

First published 1967
© 1967 J. Rose

Set in Times New Roman and printed in
Great Britain by Richard Clay (The Chaucer Press) Ltd
Bungay, Suffolk

Preface

This book is concerned with the anatomy and physiology of automation, i.e. with its structure, tools and working concepts. The uses and effects of automation on the economy and society are described and discussed in another volume in this series (*Automation: its uses and consequences*).

Automation is designed for the intelligent layman who wishes to acquire a basic knowledge of this subject without excessive mathematical or technical detail. The book is also suitable for those who wish to obtain a firm foothold in the domain of automation by gaining some basic knowledge and then extending it by means of specialised books. Lists of relevant books are given at the end of each chapter.

Chapter 1 deals with the First and Second Industrial Revolutions and with tools of the latter, i.e. computers; the difference between automation and mechanisation is stressed, and various automation systems are classified. The second chapter is concerned with the basic concept of automation – the principle of feedback or closed-loop control; an elementary mathematical treatment is given at the end of the chapter. The final chapter deals with the arms and characteristic features of automatic control, as well as with the objectives and types of control systems, including optimisation methods. The book ends with a glossary of relevant terms and an index.

I wish to express my thanks to all those who assisted me in this task: to Mr G. Hunter, B.Sc., C.Eng., senior lecturer, Department of Mechanical and Production Engineering, Blackburn College of Technology and Design, for his advice and corrections. I am grateful to my wife, Fay, who gave me the necessary encouragement, and thanks are due also to my sons, Paul and John, for literature searches, corrections, comments and proof-reading. Last but not least, I wish to record my gratitude to Mr I. A. G. Le Bek, editor of the C.S.P. project, for his invitation to write the book and for his useful advice.

J. ROSE

Contents

1. Cybernation

'One of the greatest pains to human nature is the pain of a new idea.'
WALTER BAGEHOT

THE FIRST AND SECOND INDUSTRIAL REVOLUTIONS

Man is not only a *Homo Sapiens* – a creature capable of forming abstract ideas and reasoning – but also a *Homo Faber*, a maker of tools. Since the dawn of civilisation, men could make tools, use them and produce more and more elaborate implements. Apart from very minor exceptions, the propensity for making tools is the sole prerogative of man in the animal kingdom; it has even been called the membership card of the human race. The stone axe of primitive man, the use of metals and the invention of the wheel are vivid examples of man's ability as a toolmaker in the beginning of civilisation. These and later, more sophisticated, additions to early man's storehouse of weapons in his fight for survival in a hostile environment display an important feature: the power used to drive these tools, whatever their complexity, was either human or animal. True, the windmill and water-mill used nature's power sources, but this represented a small fraction of the total energy expenditure.

The hallmark of the First Industrial Revolution was the substitution of mechanical power for human or animal muscle. The steam-engine of the 18th century, the internal-combustion engine and the electric and hydro-electric power generators in the 19th and 20th centuries, the nuclear power of the 20th century – all these are the tools of the First Revolution, driven by steam, oil, electricity or nuclear energy. They are mechanically driven tools, where human beings exercise control but do not supply the motive power.

1

This First Revolution was preceded by half a century of preparation, during which rural industry developed and ploughed back profits into agricultural investments, which, in turn, supported the industry. It came in Britain in the second half of the 18th century, and resulted in a large portion of the population transferring from rural to factory work, the emergence of an urban working class, sharp distinctions between capital and labour, paternalism, financial criteria of success, supremacy of accountancy and judgement and so on.

The advent of the First Industrial Revolution brought about two main results: firstly, it relieved man from supplying motive power to the manufacturing tools and thus, freed from the burden of physical labour, he could concentrate on improving the means of production; secondly, plentiful and cheap goods were produced, though simple and utilitarian, so that artisans were displaced and unemployment of unskilled labourers grew.

With increasing industrialisation, the countries of Western Europe and the U.S.A. grew richer and there was a steady improvement in the living standards of the developing nations. But while the machine freed man from physical burdens and enriched society, its march of progress brought untold miseries upon millions, due mainly to the inability of man to rule the apocalyptic beast of the mechanically driven tool. The First Revolution, or the Age of Mechanisation as it is sometimes called, just progressed inexorably and ponderously, producing dreadful results, such as gross social injustices, slum cities and rape of the industrial landscape; a new industrial organisation arose, with its class divisions, dominated by a hierarchy of control. Man controlled the machines to produce goods, but did not know how to deal with the social and economic consequences of his inventions and actions.

The Second Industrial Revolution

This Revolution, or the Age of Automation, began a few decades ago. Though it is still in its infancy, it has already been subjected to intense study by scientists, economists, social workers, technologists, politicians and philosophers.

The Age of Automation, based on the technology of information, goes back to that fateful day in 1901 when Marconi sent a radio signal across the Atlantic. In a way, this achievement was a revolt against established ideas. It is interesting to relate that Marconi carried out his experiments against the scientific beliefs of his times; thus he stated (Marconi, 1932), 'Long experience has . . . taught me not always to believe in the limitations indicated by purely theoretical considerations or even by calculations'; he doubted the premises but not the electromagnetic theory itself. The implications of this breakthrough in telecommunications were enormous in the field of marine practice, broadcasting, spread of popular sciences, war, development of new industries, etc. This, in turn, led to radar and digital computers, since out of telecommunication technology came applications of automatic control based on feedback, cybernetics, information theory and automation. Other branches of science also prospered, all seemingly in a spirit of rebellion against authoritarianism, constituting a challenge to established practices. It is interesting to note that according to some psychologists and sociologists (Feuer, 1963), the scientific movement was born from a hedonist-libertarian spirit, traits of which are freedom from a sense of 'primary guilt' and 'asocial' attitudes bordering on subversion. Scientists are thus supposed to be disposed to oppose the strong authority of priests, elders and those with a sense of tradition. Be this as it may, the emergence of the new Age was accompanied by an upheaval in scientific thought, resulting in the elimination of many cherished traditional ideas.

The Second Industrial Revolution has also brought about the emergence of new problems in various spheres, including the structure of society. In the United Kingdom, for instance, a new class is beginning to take shape, not the old *élite* based on industrial traditions and Public School, but a class of professionals, as opposed to the enterprising amateurs of the First Industrial Revolution. This is a class based on qualifications and membership of learned societies, professional institutions and universities, leavened by vast numbers of engineers and technologists produced by increasing numbers of centres of higher technological and scientific training. To them, industrial developments and research departments are not frivolities and eccentric items on the debit side of the ledger. Their brains are capital and not labour, and the power of this new breed of scientists and technologists is inherent in its personal creative abilities, so necessary for modern industry. This new social stratum does not expect to conform to the traditional structure of industry, however modernised; its members insist on having a say in the policy of the employing firm, and they are inclined to revolt against the sacred cow of accounts and short-term views of the 'old school'. This is particularly true of the U.S.A., where scientists and technologists hold a substantial part of the equity of the firms. In addition, a number of small and specialised companies have been formed by scientists and engineers with the sole object of applying scientific innovation on a commercial scale.

Apart from this and allied social currents, the Age of Automation is bringing about vast changes in the economic, social and educational fields, which will be discussed in *Automation: its uses and consequences*. The welfare and future of mankind demands that remedial action be taken in good time to reduce the deleterious effects of those changes in this so-called 'accidental century' in order not to repeat the mistakes of the First Revolution. But before proceeding with this, to obtain a proper understanding of the problems it is necessary to analyse the two revolutions in terms of the basic differences, which are mechanisation and automation, and study the interaction between the 'brain' and 'weapons' of automation.

MECHANISATION AND AUTOMATION

There appears to be some confusion concerning the terms 'mechanisation' and 'automation'. The term 'automation' is sometimes attributed to Del S. Harder, Vice-President of Manufacturing at the Ford Motor Company, and sometimes to John Diebold, President of the U.S. Diebold Group of Management Consultant Companies. The former referred to automation as the use of mechanical handling between transfer machines (Ashburn, 1962), i.e. the linking together of machine tools into a continuous production line by mechanical devices to load, unload and transfer a workpiece between stations of a single machine or between stations of different machines; this is now known as 'Detroit Automation'. Diebold (1962), on the other hand, gives a number of definitions. Some of these are: (*a*) automation is a philosophy of technology – a set of concepts; (*b*) if automation means anything at all, it means more than a mere extension of mechanisation; (*c*) automation is a new way of analysing and organising work; (*d*) the fundamental importance of automation is not so much the connecting of machines as it is the ability to create automatic information and control systems. It is essential to note that Detroit Automation is really an extension of mechanisation, while Diebold's various definitions are not sufficiently comprehensive, nor do they stress the importance of feedback control, as will be seen later.

The difference between the two is crucial. Mechanisation, or automaticity, however complex, involves machines which do work, but operators are required to control them in detail and to instruct them at every stage what they are to do next; thus mechanisation is a process of replacing human labour by machine labour. On the other hand, automation is not a more refined form of mechanisation or ultra-mechanisation, but *a qualitatively different process* that eliminates both human labour and detailed human control; the automated machine controls itself throughout long sequences of tasks, i.e. the process is conducted automatically without human intervention to predetermined requirements, which may or may not have been extrinsically set by a human being.

The essential difference between mechanisation and automation is based on the presence of the closed-loop or feedback control in the latter (see chapter on feedback), which enables the machine to control its performance at any moment by means of data supplied by the control unit that supervises the operation. The distinguishing characteristic of modern automatic machines is that they contain some form of sensing organ, and a feedback path from the sensing organ to the

actuator. Thus, the conveyor-belt system in a motor-car factory
is an example of a highly mechanised operation; while a
modern version of a steel rolling mill is an example of automation, which uses a number of control systems, all involving
feedback, to maintain the finished width and thickness of
steel; at every stage of this process, information is being
supplied via the closed loop from the working area to the
control and actuating systems; in effect, the complex machine
system controls its own performance, working to set standards
and requirements. This system could also be expanded to
include the automatic setting of requirements by information
arriving from selling outposts, arranging priorities and storing
the manufactured goods ready for despatching to a given
destination. Modern automation thus makes use of machines
which are capable of simulating to some extent the human
neuromuscular and even the psychoneuromuscular systems,
feedback being the common concept. Feedback control is
accomplished by feeding back either continuously or inter-
mittently part of the output signal (response) of the system, so
that comparison can be made by the control unit with the
input signal (command), which enables the system to make its
own adjustments. Feedback control technology – a new
development since 1940 in its effective form – enables these
error-correcting procedures, and many others of similar
nature, to be carried out continually without human intervention. This technology permits design of control mechanisms
which are electromechanical analogues of the human neuromuscular system.

While the principle of feedback forms the basis of
automation, its brain is the computer, mainly the digital
type. Computers are capable of storing, processing and
analysing masses of data supplied by sensing devices, via the
closed-loop system of the feedback mechanism, and of carrying out decision-making on the basis of this intellectual activity.
Thus the merging of the feedback mechanism, the equivalent
of the neuromuscular system of man, with computers has
produced an equivalent of a psychoneuromuscular system
(Reintjes, 1962), e.g. numerically or tape-controlled machines.

Thus automated assemblies not only serve as replacements for man's muscular energy, but they can also simulate to some extent his nervous system and imitate, in a crude way at present, some of his mental power. The computer has become an extension of man's intellect and the machine his muscle, both of these being combined by feedback into a mechanism of prodigious power and performance. These machines can sometimes carry out operations more effectively than humans, as in procedures involving a combination of mathematical operations with highly agile manipulative skill. The possibilities for machines which can attain exceedingly high levels of sophistication are enormous, and in the search for the design and building of such machines important clues will be yielded by the performance of man's psychoneuromuscular system. In order to define automation more closely, it is therefore preferable to use the term 'cybernation', as proposed by Sir Leon Bagrit in his Reith Lectures, so that the intellectual foundations of this phenomenon and underlying ideas can be made evident and the false overtones of ultra-mechanisation or automaticity eliminated. Indeed, automation is one of the aspects of cybernetics, the theory of communication and control.

AUTOMATA

The science of cybernetics is concerned with the amalgamation of two allied fields: (i) human cybernetics, i.e. the study of the workings of the human mind; and (ii) robot cybernetics concerned with the mode of operation of computing devices. These two aspects are quite related, the study of one throwing light on the other, while the robot gadgets used in cybernetics are largely attempts to imitate the human mind and nervous system in the fields of planned and corrective control. The stage has now been reached when machines can be constructed which can make independent decisions, i.e. their course of action is determined by whether or not certain conditions have been satisfied.

This description opens, however, a large loop-hole in the proper designation of machines in the context of automation. Thus a lock in a door will fit this definition, since the decision (the way in which the key turns in the lock and unlocks it) depends on the shape of the key (condition); hence the introduction of the term automaton or robot, i.e. a machine that is intentionally designed to be able to make decisions.

The automata, which are generally electronic circuits but could also be 'light' pipes or fluid devices, perform three functions: transport, selection and storage. In the electronic variety, it is electromagnetic energy which is stored or transported across a wire, while a switch is incorporated in the circuit that determines whether or not a current or voltage will pass, depending on conditions. The energy is stored in the memory element, a circuit unit with a certain number of stable states (usually two) in which it can remain indefinitely. It must be remembered, however, that the automaton, consisting of the conductor, switch and memory element, really stores and transports signals, usually defined as physical, chemical or physico-chemical phenomena, indicating the result of a previously made selection (Schuh, 1965); the meaning or interpretation of the message – the result of the selection itself – is termed information. Systems built up of elements that perform the functions of signal storage, transport and switching are termed logical nets. If a signal can assume v different values or forms and if, on the average, all v values appear equally often, then the signal is considered to have a content of $\log_2 v$ bit (logarithm of v to the base 2). The bit (a contraction of binary digit) is the smallest unit of signal content, this content having only two values which, on the average, appear equally often. If the signal content is 1 bit, then the signal is bivalent, while a signal that can assume three values has a content of $\log_2 3$, i.e. 1·58 bit, and is said to be trivalent; the usual signalling at present is bivalent, the others being too complex in practice. If signalling is done by elementary means, i.e. a signal that passes along a single wire which can only assume a finite number (usually two) of different forms, then one is dealing with digital signalling, and the corresponding automata are termed 'digital'. On the other hand, analogue signalling is concerned with signals which can assume any value of a given range, and automata making use of this are known as analogue automata. The two types of signalling may exist side by side in the same automaton.

The complete automaton

The equivalent of the human nervous system, i.e. the complete automaton, is a synthesis of five functions: sensing and recognition, program memory, process memory (or know-how), ability to make decisions, and physical control.

The first function involves two different phenomena: sensing and recognition. The former is concerned in human beings with the transmission of total wanted information from matter to mind; in robots this is equivalent to the transfer of total wanted information (data) from the surroundings or a physical process to the data handler by means of artificial sensors and communication links. These sensors may be instruments which are capable of sensing light (photocells), pressure changes (gauges), temperature changes (thermocouples) or chemical analysers, such as spectrophotometers or gas chromatographs for analysing substances. On the other hand, recognition involves more complex phenomena, which include elements of memory and comparison, and it is concerned with identifying quality and quantity. Man may have to recognise or identify another man by involving his sense of sight, and by his ability to compare the image with details lodged in his memory. An automaton can have amplitude recognition, i.e. recognise 'temperature', 'weight' or 'humidity', and also quality recognition, i.e. recognise general classes of things, such as the presence of chemicals in a manufacturing process. Each of these cases involves sensing by suitable sensors, classifying data and comparing these with data stored in the memory of the robot. These quality recognition devices are quite complex, and they are commonly used in the chemical industry, where analytical instruments can identify the desired compounds and then analyse them.

The second function is that concerned with the program memory or intermediate data processing, i.e. analysis of a command instruction involving a given target into various actions required to achieve the objective. The command program itself may assume different forms, as follows:

1. *Sequential program*, i.e. instructions carried on punched paper tape or magnetic tape for every consecutive step of a process leading to an end product.

2. *End-point program*, which is a synthesis of the sequential program, specifies the overall result desired at the end of a process, and is thus a policy statement referring to the whole industrial operation.

3. *Matrix program*, corresponding to a set of parallel or simultaneous command instructions that have to be executed together, e.g. adding together at the same time a number of different chemical compounds in various amounts to a reaction vessel in a chemical process; the information for this program is usually carried on a punched card.

4. *Sequential-matrix program* is the most important in automation. It is concerned with parallel and consecutive instructions, e.g. instructions to aircraft present at different heights above the airport to drop to a given altitude, different for each aircraft (matrix data), while dealing consecutively with aircraft arriving within a period of several hours in the same or different way (sequential data). This set of commands can be carried by multi-track magnetic tape, which can memorise several sets of data at the same time and also remember data in correct order.

The third function of a complete automaton relates to the knowledge of the probable reaction of a process to instructions contained in the command program. In other words, the built-in 'know-how' in the robot must be capable of modifying programs to attain a given objective under all practical conditions. To accomplish this difficult task, it is essential to build into the robot a knowledge of all casual laws that are likely to play a part in the process. This is done by expressing these in the form of mathematical and logical laws and by introducing these relations into a mathematical robot, which may be a digital or analogue computer (the latter deals with simulation of calculations by way of proportions, the former by way of numbers). This robot will then react to different sets of circumstances, brought to its 'knowledge' by sensing devices in accordance with certain mathematical laws. This simulation of process know-how is by no means an easy task, since an enormous amount of data must be specified in every detail. In fact, very few processes can at present be simulated in this way. For example, the preparation of an optimum production schedule (progress of various jobs, priorities, etc.) in a factory containing several departments with different types of machines, each capable of doing many specific jobs, involves an enormous amount of calculation, particularly since machines break down, raw materials do not arrive on time or workers are absent. In practice, a team of 'process chasers' or 'progress clerks' are employed, whose function is really to improvise ways of making up for various deficiences. In theory, it is possible to allow for all contingencies, but in even medium-size factories or workshops the amount of calculation is overwhelming. Thus in a single large factory the number of possible schedules for a single week's work may be a figure of over 100 digits. In other words, a team of clerks would have to spend several centuries to decide the best way of arranging next week's work! Even a computer could not do justice to this job.

There is, however, another way of tackling this vast problem by computer. The machine is programmed to use a statistical approach, i.e. by combining the priorities and other variables in a purely random way in a process equivalent to tossing a coin. The computer compares thousands of different schedules in a matter of hours; the same task would occupy a clerk several centuries. In practice, the computer generally supplies information about the probable optimum schedule which is economical to run and quite satisfactory.

The ability to make decisions is the fourth function of an automaton. The robot, having 'received information', 'compared' this with the program and 'consulted' this with its memory, has now to make a decision that will give rise to an unambiguous action. This action may be of the 'yes' or 'no', or 'more or less' variety, the latter being quantitative: i.e. 'How much more or less?' The robot has to take a logical decision and act accordingly. The actual action is achieved by electronic means, such as transistors or servo-mechanisms, thus constituting the fifth function of physical control.

The synthesis of these five functions is embodied in the total automaton, which is capable of simulating the workings of the human mind in the execution of certain tasks. The robot is thus endowed with a 'brain', or data-processing centre, which knows 'all' about the process and can take decisions by analysing the data fed into it and modify its instructions in the light of its know-how so as to achieve a given objective in accordance with the command program; these decisions may then be translated into action by actuating devices (Fig. 1).

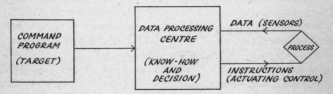

Fig. 1. *The total automaton.*

NEURAL AND ELECTRONIC LOGICAL NETS

The study of logical nets, as defined above, throws some light on the working of the human brain. In terms of elementary units the brain has probably the capacity of a million large electronic computers, and occupies a small fraction of their volume. But the units in the computer can react about a million times faster than the nervous cells (or neurons) in the brain, with their associated switches (synapses) and conductors (axons). Moreover, even if an electronic computer were built with the same number of units as the brain and then were asked a simple question, such as 'Who was Einstein?', this giant machine could not possibly supply an answer any faster than a man, if at all, since the human brain makes use of switching and other constructional principles, as well as endless numbers of permutations of interconnections not yet available in the most advanced computers. Furthermore, it is probable that the structures of the two types of logical nets are based on realising the logical operations 'or', 'and' and 'not', though these operations are used in very different ways in the two types of nets; it is impossible to imagine, for instance, that an electronic circuit, however complex, can have anything like feelings, creative thinking or a willingness to sacrifice its safety for an ideal. In general, while a robot may, in theory, be capable of dealing with recursive functions in logic, i.e. a succession of steps, each of which is uniquely determined by preceding steps, it is quite unable to tackle irrecursive functions, i.e. functions for which a uniquely determined way of solving cannot be given. (Gödel, 1931.)

REDUNDANCY IN CYBERNETIC SYSTEMS

There is also another area of fundamental difference between the human brain and automaton, viz. redundancy. If one adopts a cybernetic point of view, the human brain is considered to be a very reliable machine made up of a vast number (about 10 000 million) of individually unreliable components (neurons). Thus a little alcohol can change the performance of millions of neurons; and each neuron – a computing element – is liable to degenerate and die without any replacement being available, since these nervous cells do not undergo division in the adult. The links between the neurons are tenuous; there are invariably areas of injured tissue, and emotional disturbances affecting millions of neurons may be severe. Yet the brain serves man incredibly well. It does this by incorporating redundant inputs and nodes; by having extra units and connections, i.e. redundancy, the overall reliability is increased.

Stafford Beer (1964) has calculated that the human brain has a redundancy of the order of 20 000 : 1. Hence it is capable of some rational work even where under the influence of alcohol or drugs, for it generates variety both structurally and operationally by means of its host of redundant units and connections. The brain does not stop functioning for maintenance periods, since it can accommodate the unreliability of its components. The theorems and the logic of neural nets, as applied to the brain, are known and explain how this defective apparatus is able to deal with some nearly impossible situations. On the other hand, electronic or other logical nets are built into a whole without redundancy, care being taken to produce better and more reliable components. Also, these non-biological mechanisms are unable to deal with a breakdown in some components by redirecting the flow of information by different paths, as in the brain.

RELIABILITY IN AUTOMATED SYSTEMS

The problem of reliability is of the utmost importance in systems involving advanced automation. In fact, a new science of reliability is now in existence which is concerned with diagnosis and rectification of faults before and during the operation of the plant, discovery of variation of performance during the lifetime of the system, design of efficient components and their connections, and building in some redundancy. In the long run, the reliability of a system depends on those of its vital components. Indeed, the overall reliability is given by the product of the individual reliabilities of the vital components. For instance, if a system consists of four vital components the reliabilities of which are 0·99, 0·80, 0·75 and 0·70, then the system reliability is equal to $0·99 \times 0·80 \times 0·75 \times 0·70 \simeq 0·41$, i.e. the system is likely to operate only 41% of the time. It is evident from the above that it is essential to use few components, each of high reliability. Furthermore, if some of the components have a low reliability, then it is essential to introduce parallel duplication or triplication systems, i.e. provide redundancy. This procedure is more useful than that of having plug-in units with a number of contacts for replacements in case of failure; the contacts themselves introduce unreliability. Actual figures for various reliabilities for various redundancies may be worked out (Foster, 1963). In any event, it is necessary to eliminate components with a reliability of less than 0·9998, i.e. two hours breakdown in 10 000 hours of operation. In addition, the system ought to include diagnostic instruments, which must not form part of the system itself, otherwise its unreliability may well be increased. Above all, it is vital to establish rigid specifications for various units, otherwise the problem of reliability becomes too difficult to handle.

In order to render automation effective, by preventing extended breakdown and by catering for temporary faults by immediate replacement, the system must be endowed with means to cope with all emergencies. Although automated systems cannot imitate the human brain with its built-in redundancy of 20 000:1, they must be constructed in such a way as to reduce to the absolute minimum any stoppages due to failures of components. Automation can only be introduced provided that the problem of reliability is overcome successfully. The present lack of confidence in reliability of electronic automation is partly responsible for the tardiness with which automation is being introduced into industry.

The concept of the total automata with the allied problems of cybernetic systems, redundancy and reliability brings us now to the subject of automation in industry. The nine automation systems, as used by industry, will be considered in the next section.

NINE AUTOMATION SYSTEMS

A useful classification of practical automation systems has been given by Foster (1963). This consists of a combination of three basic modes of automation with three material processes, the latter being molecular or chemical, single-object or shaping, and many-object or positional. These processes, which are really concerned with pattern on different scales, consist of subjecting materials to a procedure, the nature of which depends on that of the material; examples of these procedures are blast furnace, machine tool and manufacturing assembly processes, respectively. On the other hand, the three basic modes of automation are programmed automation for stable and obedient processes (e.g. control of a process by punched-card or paper-tape instructions without return of information), negative feedback corrective automation for unstable processes (e.g. a central heating system, where more heat is supplied when the temperature drops below a predetermined level),

Table 1. *The combination of the three modes of nine automation systems.*

Type of material	Mode of automation	Control	Examples
Molecular	Programmed	Batch sequence or Materials dispensing	Batch chemical or materials dispensing processes
Molecular	Negative-feedback	Continuous process stages reacting to data input from sensing devices	Continuous processes in chemical plants controlled by computers
Molecular	Sorting	Automatic analysis of random input materials to determine the possibilities of the subsequent process (feed forward control)	Manufacture of animal foodstuffs or alloying of metals
Single-object	Programmed	Shaping of materials	Tape-controlled machine tools if fine limits are not required; 'automatic' knitting machine
Single-object	Negative-feedback	Continuous control by error signals	Sheet metal rolling, numerically controlled machine tool for accurate performance
Single-object	Sorting	Dimensional grading of piece parts for selective assembly of units by automatic inspection machines	Automobile industry (automatic grading machines)
Many-object	Programmed	Control of mechanical handling and traffic	Automatic push-button lift; automatic assembler of parts
Many-object	Negative-feedback	'Navigation according to references'	Radio navigational and star guidance systems
Many-object	Sorting	Control of random input positional processes	Railway marshalling yards; mail sorting

and sorting automation for control of random-input processes (e.g. sorting of letters in a postal office, when the input of mail is random and the analysis of the process is used to modify command programs, the result of recognition only affecting *later* consequences, such as rerouting). The combination of the three modes of automation with three types of processes leads to nine automation systems. Table 1 shows the result.

Having reviewed the concept of automation in various settings, it is now necessary to turn our attention to its basis and brain. The basis of automation is the concept of feedback, while the brain is the computer. The former will be discussed in detail in Chapter 2, while the remainder of this chapter will be concerned with the latter.

THE STORY OF THE COMPUTER

The first major contribution in the field of fast calculating machines was made in 1642 by Blaise Pascal, who constructed a mechanical adding machine. In 1671 Leibniz modified Pascal's machine by adapting it to perform subtraction, multiplication, division and extraction of roots. Little further progress was made till the 19th century, when Charles Babbage (1792–1871) invented his 'Difference Engine' and then the 'Analytical Engine', the former based on an idea put forth by H. H. Müller in 1786. Babbage never completed the former and never started building the latter, though he left thousands of drawings that contain the basic principles upon which modern computers are built. The machines could, in principle, perform serial operations, i.e. a number of predetermined operations in sequence, and also select from alternatives presented to it a given course of action. The 'Difference Engine' was a special-purpose calculating device, while the 'Analytical Engine' was a universal or general-purpose machine capable, in theory, of doing any calculation whatsoever. The inventor envisaged a store of 1000 numbers, each number being represented to no less than 50 decimal places. The machine had all the parts required for a general-purpose computer. Thus it had a store for holding numbers, an arithmetical unit for performing operations in these numbers (termed 'mill' by Babbage), a control device to enable the machine to perform operations in the correct sequence, and input and output units; the information was to be fed into the machine by means of punched cards – an idea he borrowed from the Jacquard loom – while the results of calculations were to be displayed by means of punched cards or direct printing. Babbage was, however, defeated in his efforts to build the machine by the attitude of many of his influential contemporaries, and particularly by the lack of techniques of precision engineering in the 19th century, when even simple reliable desk calculators could not be made in quantity.

Babbage was a man of many parts. He invented the ophthalmoscope; he calculated the statistical tables on which modern insurance is based; he devised what is now known as operational research; and he showed how to make postal charges economic. He was a Fellow of the Royal Society, one of the first trustees of the British Association for the Advancement of Science, a founder member of the Royal Astronomical Society and the first Chairman of the Statistical Society of London. His friends and acquaintances included royalty, Charles Dickens and great mathematicians such as Laplace and Fourier. His great wealth, a Government grant of £17 000 and influential friends enabled him to start building the 'Difference Engine'. He was, however, ahead of his time, so that frustrations coupled with a lack of tact gave rise to endless squabbles and bitterness. Few people mourned his death in 1871, though many newspapers contained conventional obituaries. It is only thanks to Lord Bowden, Principal of the Manchester University Institute of Science and Technology, who did some original historical research for his book *Faster than thought*, that Babbage's name is familiar to computer technologists and learned institutions.

It is interesting to note that Babbage enjoyed great support from a brilliant woman mathematician, Ada Augusta, Countess of Lovelace, the only child of the poet Lord Byron, who actually planned problems for the machine and formulated a schedule of instructions (program) to enable the engine to carry out a desired calculation automatically; she was, in fact, the first programmer ever. Over a century later another gifted woman, Dr Hopper of the U.S.A., made an important advance in programming by creating the idea of compilers.

Babbage's work was forgotten, despite his efforts to attract interest and the constant battles for the recognition of his brilliant ideas. He suffered the unhappy fate of a misunderstood genius, and it has taken the world a century to catch up with his ideas.

Fourteen years after Babbage's death in 1871, the statistician Herman Hollerith, in the U.S.A., resurrected the idea of punched cards for the purpose of speeding up the completion of the U.S. population census. He punched holes in cards to represent the information obtained and collated the data by means of electrical accounting machines, completing the census in about one-third of the time the previous one had taken. Following this success, Hollerith formed a company to manufacture calculating machines; this company became the nucleus of the mighty International Business Machines.

The next stage in this story is the construction of a 'differential analyser' machine in 1925 by Vannevar Bush at the Massachusetts Institute of Technology. In order to solve the problem of powering the long train of gears, Bush used mechanical torque-amplifiers between the stages. However, Bush's machine was of the analogue type (in which a number is represented by a physical phenomenon, such as variation of a voltage or the sliding of a rod, e.g. a speedometer or a slide rule), while Babbage's engine was of a digital type, in which numbers are stored as whole numbers and not as fractions of the unit. Two copies of Bush's machine were constructed in the 1930s for ballistic research and electrical engineering.

In the same decade L. J. Comrie in Great Britain and W. J. Eckert in the U.S.A. pioneered the first scientific computation of astronomical data using business data handling equipment, while G. R. Stibitz at the Bell Telephone Company's laboratories in the U.S.A. designed a relay-type semi-automatic machine with teletypewriter known as the 'Complex Computer'.

The first fully automatic, though electromechanical, computer was constructed in 1944 by a team led by Dr H. Aiken of Harvard. This machine, called the 'Automated Sequence Controlled Calculator' and designated Mark 1, was based on Babbage's ideas of the 'Analytical Engine', though it did not have the capability to choose between alternatives, i.e. branching operations. This machine was later modified to include valves and solid-state techniques, but it had no stored programs and was operated almost entirely by mechanical switches.

Modern computers

A digital electronic computer is a machine that is capable of handling information in numerical form and performing at high speed a number of arithmetical or logical operations on this information in a given sequence; a digital computer counts, while an analogue computer measures, i.e. represents variables by physical analogies. The digital computer consists of five parts (Fig. 2), viz. input, output (such as punched cards, paper tape or magnetic tape; line printer for output only), storage, arithmetic unit and control unit. The function of the control unit is to instruct the other parts to carry out certain operations. The storage consists of an immediate access or working store and a backing store, the latter for holding information. The working store is much more expensive than the backing store, its capacity ranging, in general, from 4000 to 100 000 numbers. In modern computers this store consists of magnetic cores which have the facility of taking or giving information very quickly (in a few microseconds). The backing store, less expensive and containing greater holding capacity (over a million numbers), may consist of magnetic tape, magnetic drums, magnetic card file or disc stores. Some of the store is occupied by the programming instructions, the remainder is used for storing data, placing intermediate results, etc. A program is a set of instructions to direct the computer to perform a desired operation or solve a predefined problem. The term 'software' applies to general-purpose programs used to extend the capabilities of computers, and it includes compilers, assemblers, monitors, executive routine and all the programs and routines used to operate the computer; it differs from 'hardware', the actual machine parts and devices which make up a computer. The number representation system commonly

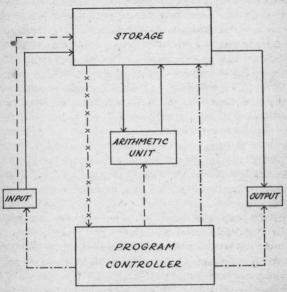

Fig. 2. *Digital computer.* (—— *Data flow;* – – – – *Program flow;* – x – x – *Instructions to program controller;* – · – · – *control exercised.*)

used is binary notation, i.e. a system with a base of two, in which decimal digits are represented by means of only two symbols – zero and one.

Though various inventors * have claimed the credit for the resurrection of Babbage's ideas in an electronic setting with operation in the binary notation, the father of the present-day electronic computers is undoubtedly ENIAC (Electronic Numerical Integrator and Computer) designed and built by

* For examples, see William Phillips' claim in the *Sunday Times*, 5 September 1965.

J. Mauchley and J. P. Eckert in 1945 for the Army, which
found Mark 1 too slow for its requirements. ENIAC was a
giant unit containing 6000 switches, 18 000 valves, 5000 terminals and 500 000 soldered joints, but it had no gears,
counting being done by electronic pulses. The machine could
perform automatically sequenced operations at high speed;
thus, it could add numbers at a rate of 5000 per second, i.e.
15 000 times as fast as the rate of Mark 1. The input was
electromechanical, the output was a punch card, and the
machine stored its instructions internally, i.e. it did not require rolls of paper tape. These instructions had, however, to
be wired into the machine by connecting appropriate circuits.
This tedious operation, which required several days for wiring
in instructions for a program, was eliminated by Burks,
Goldstein and von Neumann, who designed a stored program
computer EDSAC, and by Mauchley and Eckert, who constructed a similar machine known as EDVAC.

The theoretical groundwork for building computers was
done by J. von Neumann in a series of reports at the Institute
of Advanced Studies at Princeton in 1945–47. These principles
related to the use of a machine language, i.e. a computer is
designed to be able to read, interpret and execute a sequence
of instructions; the separation of computer functions, con-
ceptual or physical, by having separate operation, control,
memory, input and output units, was another of the basic
principles studied. Another idea produced by von Neumann
was that of a flow diagram, which provides a completely
precise specification of the entire computational process; this
is a powerful aid for solving difficult and novel problems in
the physical sciences. It was on the basis of these ideas that
von Neumann had proceeded after the Second World War to
build a computer at the Institute for Advanced Studies. This
machine, called the von Neumann Princeton or IAS machine,
and based on his fundamental paper *Preliminary discussion of
the logical design of an electronic computing instrument* published in 1946 (a joint paper by von Neumann, Goldstein and
Burks), became the prototype of many other machines, including the MANIAC 1 of Los Alamos (U.S.A.), ORACLE

at Oak Ridge (U.S.A.), SILLIAC at Sydney (Australia), the I.B.M.-701, and even modern machines as far as the logical structure is concerned.

This lead by the U.S.A. is still maintained at the present time, not only in computer development but also in the number of computer installations; in 1966 27 000 out of all the 35 000 computer installations were in the U.S.A. On the other hand, the United Kingdom has made important original contributions, apart from Babbage's basic concepts, to computer development by being first in the field of workable electrostatic storage devices and commercially available electronic computers. Furthermore, while the U.K. Government agencies paid little attention to this subject, the U.S. Army, Navy and the Bureau of Standards embarked upon an ambitious programme of constructing advanced computers and spearheading training programmes for personnel and computer mathematicians. Moreover, the U.S. Office of Naval Records built a fast machine in its time, the Whirlwind II, which contained a new type of memory, a magnetic core memory instead of the much more limited electrostatic memory.

The next stage of development was the construction of a 'real-time' (as it happens) machine, i.e. speed of operation is concurrent with the incoming data, the computer SAGE (Senior Automatic Ground Environment) at the Massachusetts Institute of Technology in the early 1950s. Its object was to interpret data gathered by radar about enemy aircraft and to compute trajectories for missiles for destroying these targets in flight. In addition, SAGE had to store enormous amounts of data and offer means for immediate filing, rearranging and retrieval of information. Hence enormous speeds and capacities were necessary. Moreover, this equipment ('hardware') could not perform without programming ('software'), so that a vast organisation ('The Rand') was established to program the SAGE machine. This enormous burden – since this computer knew only what it was told in most perfect detail – was somewhat reduced by the introduction of compilers (automatic computer coding system that translates a program into machine language), i.e. machines which act as sort of middle-men between man and computer, and places part of the programming work upon the latter. Indeed, the widespread use of computers has been attained only through the break-through of programming by means of compilers. This and other modifications became even more necessary when the Ballistic Missile Early Warning System (BMEWS) was established at a cost of over £300 million in the early 1960s, to counteract the threat of ballistic missiles to the North American Continent.

In the late 1950s computers became the business of large teams of specialists and not of individual inventors as before, and a new industry grew up – the electronic computer in-dustry. Despite the evident potential of these machines, there was no conviction that computers were a saleable commodity and a real necessity. The introduction of Card Programmed Calculator (CPC) is thought to have tipped the scales towards commercial production and use. The first of these com-mercial machines – the Sperry Rand Corporation UNIVAC – were ordered by the U.S. Air Force and Army; this was cautiously followed by the General Electric Company and Metropolitan Insurance Company for use in data processing. Even the giant International Business Machines Company had misgivings until it sold 19 of its I.B.M.-701 machines for defence purposes. This 'large' order induced this company to proceed with the development of machines for scientific and business use – the I.B.M.-650 in 1953, of which about 2000 were eventually built. At the same time, I.B.M. produced a computer language known as SPEEDCODE. Contacts between users and enthusiasts grew by means of publications and meetings. Thus Fred Gruenberger published the first news-sheet in the computing field, *Computing News*, while groups of users were organised in order to eliminate redundant effort on systems and programs. An enormous computer-manu-facturing industry has grown up in the last decade, and the number of users has multiplied at a tremendous rate. At * the

* *The Times Review of Industry and Technology*, February 1966, pp. 11–12, U.K.

beginning of 1961 there were 5000 computers installed in the U.S.A., in 1964 the number had reached 20 000. European countries are behind the U.S.A. in this respect. For example, in 1964 there were 1160 computers in the United Kingdom, 1600 in West Germany and 1060 in France. A comparison of these figures has, however, limited significance, since computers vary tremendously in size and, even more, by the degree of utilisation.

Poor utilisation of computers is a serious problem. Expensive computer equipment is very often used at a fraction of its capacity, mainly because the machine is being at times mistakenly adapted to a pre-computer era organisation, while the staff have but a vague idea of the potential of their firm's new tool. Effective education of systems analysts and computer programmers is essential to ensure the proper use of this expensive equipment, while management will also have to be enlightened as to the real significance of computers. Firms will have to use novel techniques to study the best use of computers and, indeed, to make decisions regarding their purchase and usage. One of these techniques is S.C.E.R.T. (Systems Computer Evaluation and Review Technique), developed in 1964 by Comress of Washington, D.C.; it is a collection of computer programs designed to select the best available machine and programs for a given job. Information about the firms that want to buy a machine is fed into a powerful computer, which then creates a mathematical model of the company and selects the best installation and programs for its requirements.

The problem of misuse of computers in the United Kingdom is quite serious, particularly if coupled with other failings in the field of automation. Professor S. Gill, Director of the Regional Computer Centre in London, is reported in *The Guardian* to have told a meeting of the Association for Science Education in London in 1965 that 'Britain's failure to rise to the occasion after leading in the field of computers is one of the biggest national tragedies of this century. . . . Whereas in 1950 we were leading the world in this subject, we have completely and utterly failed to rise to the occasion. We are now even falling behind the rest of the Western World in the rate we are developing and exploiting computers.' About 40% (by number) of the computers installed in the United Kingdom are of foreign origin, while the number of computers per million of population in 1965 was 21 (the corresponding figures for the U.S.A., West Germany and France being 105, 29, and 22 respectively). Of the total stock of computers in the United Kingdom, the main manufacturing industries account for about one half, while the other half is shared between computer manufacturers, service bureaux, research centres, universities, commercial undertakings, etc. It is interesting to note that in 1964 computers in the United Kingdom accounted for only about a quarter of the total deliveries costing £200 million of British-made electronic apparatus, while their export contribution was only about 12% of the total export value of electronic goods.

There is enormous international competition in the world's computer market, which is dominated by the American I.B.M. In Europe the British computer industry is perhaps the largest, the biggest companies being I.C.T., English Electric-Leo Marconi and Elliott Automation. This battle is not fought on entirely equal grounds, since the American companies receive Government research contracts on a scale which makes the recent £5 million grant of U.K. Ministry of Technology seem very small indeed. The future for the British computer industry may well lie in the manufacture of more sophisticated computers, in computer-managed automation and in greater co-operation between the various companies, not excluding foreign ones. Developments, such as relatively cheap shoe-box size machines manufactured by Elliott's compared by Sir Leon Bagrit, the Chairman of Elliott Automation, to Model-T Ford cars as regards mass production, or the English Electric-Leo Marconi range of miniaturised machines, may give Britain a useful lead.

The computer industry in various countries is a growth industry *par excellence*. It is believed that in the U.S.A. the total outlay on computers will have risen in the decade between 1960 and 1970 from less than $2000 million to over

$6000 million. Furthermore, expenditure on computers will form an increasing proportion of all expenditure on new plant and equipment (Diebold, 1965). It is expected that by 1970 there will be 5000 computers in the United Kingdom alone, some of them extremely powerful and sophisticated machines. In the past decade some £60 million have been invested in Great Britain alone in computer installations, and almost every industry now makes use of these machines, which are accepted as vital tools in management, design, control, development and research. This progress is expected to continue unabated, though dwarfed by that in the U.S.A., where the computer has become a multibillion-dollar enterprise. There are signs that the battle for world-wide business among computer manufacturers is beginning to reach a ferocious intensity. The prize is high, since sales of computers to industrial nations are increasing at a rate of about 22% per annum. Though these markets are now mainly confined to the U.S.A. and Europe, it is anticipated that during the 1970s Latin American countries and the new nations of Asia and Africa will also become important outlets, particularly since the computers can multiply vastly the effective labour of a few trained operators, in factories and offices, thus compensating for illiteracy and lack of business training. Table 2 shows computer usage in various countries (Leitch, 1966). The

Table 2. *Computer usage.*

Countries	Actual 1966		Estimate 1970	
	Number of computers	Value *million dollars*	Number of computers	Value *million dollars*
U.S.A.	27 000	7 500	45 000	12 500
Western Europe	6 000	2 200	18 000	5 500
Japan	1 900	300	4 575	900
Latin America	200	25	440	115

bottleneck is the need for gigantic resources to develop computers and to overcome the shortage of specialists. This is, indeed, a game played by giants.

Miniaturisation

The next chapter in this saga of computer development was the replacement of vacuum tubes, i.e. valves, by tiny transistors, which reduced the physical size of the machines ten times, slashed costs and added greatly to reliability. This was further modified to include micro-electronic circuits as in the I.B.M. System/360 computer (1964), which may attain a primary storage capacity of eight million characters that could be expanded to hundreds of millions of characters.

This technique of micro-electronics, or micro-miniaturisation, was used in the giant UNIVAC 1050-II machines in the U.S.A., and in the 'miniaturised' computers built by Leo-Marconi and Ferranti in the United Kingdom; the latter, no bigger than a portable radio set, could control the output of an oil refinery or fly an aircraft, and possibly transform transport systems and factories. The reduction in size of circuits is essential, since the ultimate speed of the computer operation is linked to speed of light of 186 000 miles per second, i.e. one foot in one thousand-millionth of a second. The advantage of this development is not just in the reduced size (another order of magnitude) of computers, but in the tremendous increase in reliability, operating speed and considerable reduction in cost and power requirements. For instance, one version of a micro-miniaturised computer, the MONICA produced by the Autonetics Company, measures 0·15 cubic foot, operates from an internally stored program, can perform an addition in about 10 microseconds and only fails once in two years, while obeying an instruction list of 75 commands. This is not unusual when a chip of silicon measuring about $\frac{5}{1000}$ inch $\times \frac{1}{16}$ inch can accommodate 80 complete circuits consisting of transistors, diodes, resistors and other devices. The only bottleneck – at least, as far as cost is concerned – is the interconnections between these circuits and the computer. However, the possible introduction of laser diodes, phototransistors or fibre optics may produce the required breakthrough. It is believed that the use of optical fibres with laser action as transmission lines could usher in the era of nanosecond computers. Such a machine, no more complex than today's computers, would be able to do a man-year of work each second.

Other developments towards more sophisticated machines are tunnel diodes, the use of cryogenics (temperatures near the absolute zero, when some metals become superconducting, i.e. have no electrical resistance), modularity (ability to build up a large system from small parts or modules), faster and larger memories by using new materials such as laminated ferrites or chemical memories, and the use of logic other than Boolean or binary. Indeed, for certain problems involving information retrieval, cryogenic techniques or tunnel diodes are essential. This increase of one or two orders of magnitude in speed, reliability and performance will not involve a corresponding increase in costs, though Grosch's law implies that a machine that is four times as fast should cost twice as much ('Economy is as the square root of the speed'). In fact, the indications are that while the speed of computers has increased one million times in the last two decades, the cost for computation has been reduced 1000 times. It is worth noting that had this situation obtained in the car industry, the cost of parking a vehicle would greatly exceed that of the vehicle itself!

One of the main advances since 1950 was in the field of reliability. For example, a normal calculation on a computer may contain 1000 million basic operations, each probably depending on 100 electrical components. In order to be 99·9% sure that the result is not invalidated by a faulty component, each component must not make more than one mistake in 100 million million calculations. This is equivalent to a typist making only *one mistake in a million years of continuous typing*! This reliability could not have been envisaged before 1950. This vast increase in speed and reliability is not, however, matched by an increase in powerful methods in programming, hence the serious bottlenecks in using the powerful machines. A variety of hardware innovations have been introduced since 1950 to simplify procedures and speed up operations, such as floating-point operation, index

registers, arithmetic significance monitoring, indirect address-
ing and push-down storage banks. Other design ideas for
speeding up operations were those concerned with the ability
of the control unit to look ahead, while performing a given
instruction, and make preparations for the next few instructions to come. These important innovations in computer
design were followed closely by advances in software, i.e.
coding systems, programming and the library of routines for
controlling input and output formats.

The search for greater speed and reliability continues un-
abated, though even our present-day computers cannot be
fully utilised. Despite the overwhelming technical difficulties,
computers of enormous speeds, measured in nanoseconds (one
thousand-millionth of a second) are making their debut.
Recent developments in increasing the speed of computers a
thousandfold from microseconds to nanoseconds at all levels
of the computer hierarchy make it possible to solve many
complex problems in mathematics, pattern recognition,
statistical correlation and real-time control of rapidly occurring
events. Even if these computers manage to process one digit
of information at a time, rather than the handling of several
digits as on the present computers, they will only utilise a
fraction of the power consumption and hardware complexity.
This increase in speed is equal to that obtained on changing in
the 1940s from electromechanical relays to vacuum tubes. The
vastly increased speed will enable computers to handle problems involving the simulation of random processes and the
solution of complex systems of non-linear equations, which
would occupy man-years on the present-day machines, while
other controls, such as missile guidance and tracking, are only
effective when used in conjunction with a computer of enormous speed.

The difficulties in constructing such computers are enormous, since new materials, new types of circuits and memories
and new space–time relationships are required, bearing in
mind that the speed of light, which sets the minimum time
required to transfer information from one place to another, is
about one foot per nanosecond. Small nanosecond computers

have already been built, e.g. one by the UNIVAC Division of the Sperry Rand Corporation – a 100-nanosecond machine with a memory of 1024 words of 24 bits each. Sub-systems with small memories but with 30-nanosecond speeds have been constructed by R.C.A. of America, while the sub-assembly of counters, adders and short-sequence generators, built by the General Electric Company of America, has a speed of $2\frac{1}{2}$ nanoseconds per logic operation. It is believed that in the very near future reliable computers will be available with speeds characterised by add times of 25 nanoseconds, multiplication times of 60–80 nanoseconds, while their memory cycle times may approach 20 nanoseconds for memories up to several hundred words, and 100 nanoseconds for 4000–65 000 words memories.

In most problems complex calculations are performed on a large amount of data with a resulting large output of information. It is, therefore, necessary to consider not only the speed with which the computer components will operate but also that with which the problems could be solved. A nanosecond machine would hardly increase the speed of solution of problems involving masses of input and output data, though there may be some gain in cases relating to few input and output data. The difficulty lies in the preparation of a problem for the machine, which is time- and manpower-consuming, and then carrying out the computation. It is thus vital to reduce preparation time through automated programming techniques and improved machine organisation. The question of vastly increased costs of new generation of computers would, of course, have also to be considered, though in time the savings achieved could well more than cover the greater expenditure.

Although it is realised that much remains to be done in making use of the 'microsecond' type of computer, researchers are already thinking of building picosecond (10^{-12} seconds) machines. To achieve this, a technological revolution will have to take place to overcome the formidable limitation of the speed of light.

FACTS AND FANCIES

Returning to the third generation, or 'microsecond', computers, two major problems must be solved in order to make effective use of these powerful machines: those pertaining to (i) man and (ii) machine. The problem of man in the context of the computer presents several aspects. Firstly, equipment has progressed faster than people, so that continuous retraining is vital. Next, it is not possible at the present time to 'talk' to computers in ordinary language but only in more or less problem-oriented languages; the provision of this facility would enable the user to formulate clearly what he is trying to do. Another aspect is the abysmal ignorance among the general public of what computers really are; the spectre of a giant machine-brain ruling the world breeds out of ignorance and engenders fear and superstition. Furthermore, the progress of computer technology has been such that the very fabric of our society is being undermined with resultant far-reaching social and economic consequences. These difficulties must be tackled in a more enlightened way than that of the Luddites in the First Industrial Revolution in order to prevent possible grave consequences to the welfare of man.

The advent of the computer appears to have brought about the birth of a number of misconceptions * about these machines. These fancies are based on an irrational mixture of wishful thinking and fear of uncontrollable monsters; the former rests on the assumption that there is nothing new under the sun, the latter is an essential fear of the progress of science.

The most common misconception about computers is that they merely do arithmetic, i.e. they are glorified slide rules. In effect, they are manipulators of symbols. By suitable programming it is possible to establish relations between symbols, so they can be given a wide variety of meaning.

The idea that computers can only do what they are told to do is not entirely true. An analysis of computer performance

* Series of articles in the *American mathematical monthly*, 1965, **72**, No. 2.

soon shows that in moderately complex situations it is not possible on a practical level to foresee all of the possible consequences. There is a theorem that there can be no program which will analyse a general program to tell how long it will run on a machine without actually running the program or its direct simulation. This is like saying that once mathematical postulates are known, all the rest of deductive mathematics is trivial.

An allied misconception is that a machine can do nothing that we cannot do ourselves (though it can do it faster and more accurately). This is partially false, since orders of magnitude are ignored between human and computer potentialities. This is similar to saying that travelling by motor-cars or aeroplanes is no different from walking, as far as transportation is concerned (just consider walking 500 miles!). And computers are six orders of magnitude faster than hand computation, hence the effects on technology are revolutionary. Indeed, an increase of even one order of magnitude (that is, tenfold) may cause a complete revolution in economics and other fields.

Another common error is that computers make mistakes that people would not. It is obvious that here we are comparing a carelessly programmed machine with ideal human activities. The average mathematician with his slide rule and logarithmic tables will be inferior in routine work to a properly programmed computer. In this connection the comparison of the human mind and computer is irrelevant in a general sense; one can only compare them on specific tasks. Thus, as said earlier, one expects a computer to be so reliable in complex calculations as to be equivalent to a typist making one mistake in a million years of continuous typing!

The omniscient computer

In many essentially human activities the computer can beat a human being (Williams, 1962). Even in the Arts computers have been known to produce passable examples of music and poetry. An 18-year-old American student 'induced' a computer to compose the following:

Silently the crystal fields floated
Against the deserted mountainside
As the moon rose
The serene landscape glowed darkly
Suddenly the deserted fields glowed
Above the heavy guns
As the grass flashed
The darkly reality grew harshly.

Thus the spectre of an eventual 'take-over' of the world by machines, as so colourfully described by some science-fiction writers, would appear to have some substance. The usual arguments refuting this possibility are that computers do not think, can only do what they are told and they cannot interpret their own results; these are, however, shaky arguments, particularly the last two. On the other hand, the memory store of the human brain is vastly larger, though slower, than that of a large computer: the brain contains about 10 000 million nerve cells, each linked to about 10 000 others in an organised way; its capacity is said to exceed the total of the core storage of all the computers in the world today put together, but the brain is 500 000 times slower than a modern computer. Furthermore, the brain can apprehend a two-dimensional pattern of moving images because of the elaborate cross-connections. Again these two differences could be greatly narrowed down by better computer design.

There is, however, a vital difference between man and computer: the former wants to compute for reasons that may be completely unrelated to the things they wish to compute, for a man has, in addition to a brain, other systems which supply him with desires, drives and needs; computers are only brains without a body, free from impulses and desires and wishes to think. Finally, man has – according to Professor Williams (loc. cit.) – three advantages over the computer: no computer comparable to the human brain could be housed in a unit weighing about 150 lb, man needs far less energy than his machine counterpart and man can be produced entirely by 'unskilled labour' – a jocular remark, no doubt, but carrying overtones of seriousness.

MAN AND MACHINE

There are two fundamental problems to be considered with regard to the effective use of computers: people and the engine. The former aspect has been discussed under Facts and Fancies. The second aspect is that of machine sophistication. Various types of computers will be considered on the following pages, but it must be emphasised here that today's computer is basically that of Babbage, as regards the logical structure, since the replacement of mechanical parts by complex electronics, optical pipes or fluid devices merely makes computing more efficient but not fundamentally different. For example, the computer is still unable to solve problems that man can handle sometimes by the rule of thumb or plain hunch, for it is not a brain. Thus the problem of hierarchy, i.e. putting together detailed items and forming a picture that is different from the parts, still eludes the most sophisticated computers of today. The computer does not 'learn'; it must be reprogrammed for each problem. It is possible that a ceiling is now being reached, and the next stage may well be a complete break with Babbage's concept towards the 'brain' principles, as embodied in perceptrons and learning machines, discussed later on.

TYPES OF MODERN COMPUTERS

Computers in use at the present time fall broadly into three main categories: digital, analogue and hybrid.

A digital machine is one in which numbers are stored as whole numbers, while in an analogue computer numbers are represented by a physical phenomenon, such as variation of voltage or sliding of a rod, so that the number varies continuously within a limited range instead of altering by discrete units; a car speedometer and a slide rule are examples of an analogue operation, while the digital operation is represented by the mileage recorder or calculating machine. The analogue machines are fast, but much less accurate than the digital ones. The hybrid type is a mixed analogue and digital machine, where the latter performs parts of computation which must be done with high accuracy, while the less critical parts of the operation are performed by the much faster analogue partner. An example of this operation is the automation control of chemical processing. There, the rates of flow of fluids vary continuously, i.e. are analogue in nature but must be converted to digital measure to enable the digital computer to control the process in an accurate manner; the signals must be converted into an analogue form in order to open or close valves by energising motors or hydraulic rams for fast and continuous flow control.

In general, most of the digital machines are serial in operation, i.e. the numbers stored in the machines appear in a central arithmetic unit one after another and are then added or compared with some other numbers before being returned to the memory store. The machine does arithmetic exceedingly quickly, using an enormous memory and prodigious speeds of the order of microseconds per addition; hence the machine is capable of handling complex and very large problems involving millions of operations with great accuracy. On the other hand, analogue machines are parallel devices, i.e. all the numbers represented by physical phenomena (voltages, pressures, distances, shaft positions, etc.) are all processed (additions, multiplications, integrations) simultaneously. The accuracy of an analogue machine is thus seldom greater than one part in 1000, though the speed is exceedingly greater than that of a digital computer; an error of one part in one million can be obtained in a digital machine for less than twice the cost of an error of one part in 1000; this is impossible in the case of an analogue machine. This relatively low accuracy may be acceptable, since in many problems the accuracy of the physical data is less than that of the analogue machine. Thus in nuclear reactor studies, rocket systems and complex problems, e.g. non-linear systems, analogue computers are the most economical to use, particularly since parts of the physical system investigated can sometimes be included in the analogue set-up. Moreover, the digital machine needs skilled personnel to program it, while the analogue machine can be used by the engineer or designer, who is able to alter parameters while studying various models under different conditions. On the other hand, a large problem may tie up an analogue machine for a considerable time so that no other problem can be studied, while a digital machine, particularly the large and multi-access type, could deal with a number of problems almost simultaneously. Moreover, it is not practicable to use an analogue machine for many problems where high accuracy is necessary. For compilation of mathematical tables, solution of sets of linear equations, accurate evaluation of integrals or data processing, a digital computer is essential.

There is a minor class of problem for which the analogue computer is too inaccurate and the digital computer is too slow. The solution to this problem is based on using the simultaneous or sequential incremental computers. The first of its kind was the MADDIDA (Magnetic Drum Digital Differential Analyser) machine developed in the early 1950s in the U.S.A., which contained a digital integrator that could integrate with respect to any variable, thus conferring a higher accuracy on the operation. Subsequent machines contained many separate integrators, which made this computer rather expensive. Thus the simultaneous incremental machine costs ten times as much as the corresponding analogue machine. For some problems, however, the use of these machines is of great benefit, particularly in the aircraft industry.

Fluid computers

The digital fluid (liquid or gas) computer is worthy of mention. These types of machine, using any of a number of liquids or gases instead of electric currents, have greater reliability than electronic computers even under adverse environments. The electronic computer is liable to be troublesome even under suitable conditions, and may become quite inoperable under adverse conditions, such as during missile launching, radiation environment in nuclear power stations, or under the extreme conditions of temperature in outer space. Furthermore, no transducers are required in many applications, since pneumatic inputs from sensing elements can be fed directly into logic circuits, while the output can control or activate automatic typewriters or valves in process control. Moreover, it is believed that these fluid computers can be competitive with their electronic equivalents (Wood & Fox, 1964), provided mass-production techniques could be developed for fluid-logic circuits, using plastics as materials.

These computers contain fluid-logic devices involving the basic 'flip-flop', i.e. on (pressure of flow) and off (absence of flow), based either on the 'Coanda effect', involving the interaction of an input jet of fluid with an entrained fluid, or the NOR gate, which produces an output (one) when there is no input (zero). It must be stressed, however, that apart from technical difficulties, involving interconnections and instrumentation, one of the major impediments to the widespread use of fluid computers is their low speed. There are already fluid-logic elements that switch in about 100 microseconds, but the overall rate is limited to 1000 microseconds, three orders of magnitude slower than the electronic machines.

The limitation is, of course, due to maximum fluid-jet velocities attainable in small passages; these velocities are limited by the sonic choking of orifices at about Mach number 0·7 in gases and by the cavitation or the formation of 'vacuum bubbles' in liquids at limiting speeds; the sizes of the elements and acoustic principles will also impose limitations on speeds of response ('switching speeds') of fluid-logic units.

The considerable reliability of fluid computers is, however, of fundamental importance. The number of expected failures for the components of electronic-logic devices and fluid-logic devices under various conditions are shown in Table 3 (Wood and Fox, loc. cit., pp. 677–678). The difference between the corresponding number of failures of the two types of devices is especially striking under extreme conditions, such as extremes of temperature, strong vibration or intense radiation.

These fluid computers are, however, slow compared to their electronic equivalents. Hence their use will be somewhat limited to operations where enormous speeds are not essential. There are many servo systems in which a reliable fluid computer could do the job at a much reduced price, e.g. steering

Table 3. *Number of failures of equivalent electronic and fluid-logic devices under various conditions (unity under ordinary conditions).*

Conditions		*Cis*-lunar space	−50°C	+150°C	Solar flare in *cis*-lunar space	Single A-bomb explosion (5 miles from 20 mega-tons)	Missile vibra-tion	Partially shielded nuclear reactor
Number of failures (× 10⁻⁶ h)	Electronic	5·2	13	26	26	260	2340	2600
	Fluid	41·4	83	83	83	207	414	414

of a ship, calculation or office-machine data-handling equipment. Other systems where the fluid computers may be potentially useful are machine-tool control, training simulators, process control equipment and various servomechanisms. Fluid-logic devices may also be used for the control of peripheral equipment, such as teleprinter or typewriter keyboards. Some of these devices are now being mass-produced by using engraving methods. They are very accurately made and are very reliable.

THE OPTICAL COMPUTER

A computer may be regarded as a special type of communication network (Clapp & Yilmas, 1965), in which signals generated at one point travel to another point, where they are processed and interpreted giving rise to other signals. The marriage of computer technology with light as the transmission medium offers two main advantages: firstly, faster communication, though limited by the speed of light (1 foot in one nanosecond); secondly, the extremely short switching processes that occur in nature could be harnessed for producing computer elements with switching times of a million-millionth of a second by inducing atomic transitions by means of light.

The technology forming the basis of an optical computer is

still in its infancy and depends on progress made in the development of lasers, fibre optics ('light' pipes), spatial filters and pattern-recognition techniques, including recognition of speech for 'talking' directly to a computer by means of the SCEPTRON (Spectral Comparative Pattern Recogniser). Apart from the technical difficulties involved, there are two other considerations to be taken into account: the data stored in the memory have to be periodically regenerated, otherwise they are lost, unlike the situation in the electronic computer; the cost of storing a unit of information in the 'light' device is about 500 times as large as that in an equivalent electronic device. The first difficulty may possibly be overcome by combining lasers in series and by so-called optical pumping, while miniaturisation of the laser system and the storage of many bits of information in a single laser crystal may result in a significant reduction of cost. But existing technology of light devices is already ushering in the era of computers many thousand times faster than the existing fastest electronic machine.

THE LANGUAGE OF THE COMPUTER

The application of computers in industry, commerce or science is made possible by the use of *software* (the equipment itself is known as *hardware*), i.e. the preparation of a problem for input to the machine. This consists of first analysing the problem and programming, i.e. writing a graphic representation or flow chart of processes required to solve the problem (= what to do) and then preparing a block diagram (= how to do it); this diagram is then transformed by a coder into a program, which consists of two parts: *the operation*, which gives instructions what to do, and *operand*, which tells the computer where to find the information required. The completed program may be fed into the machine by means of perforated paper tape, punched cards or magnetic tape. Whatever the input, the binary system is used, i.e. all values are expressed by combinations of either 'zero' (off) or 'one' (on); the current is either off or on. The relation between decimal and binary systems is given in Table 4. The computer

Table 4. *Decimal–binary conversion.*

Decimal	0	1	2	3	4	5	6	7	8	9
Binary	0000	0001	0010	0011	0100	0101	0110	0111	1000	1001

then converts the instructions into its own machine language, since it does not speak the language in which the program is written. The middleman of this operation, the language used by the coder, is the compiler with its attendant compiler languages. The object here is to bring the language of the program fed into the computer as closely as possible to English or other human language, thus eliminating the herculean task of programming in the language of the machine itself. Investment in programming is very heavy; the U.S. Department of Defense alone spends about $80 million annually on programming.

There are now about 200 compiler languages. All programs prepared in a given compiler language look alike; it is also possible to compile a program for a given machine, then re-compile it for a different machine by altering only parts of the program. Despite this proliferation of languages, there are three main ones, Fortran, Algol and Cobol, with their various modifications. The first (*For*mula *tran*slator), developed by I.B.M., resembles the language of mathematics, and it effects an 85% reduction in the number of instructions, as compared to those needed by the machine language. It is, however, limited and not particularly efficient. Algol (*Algo*rithmic *l*anguage) developed in 1960 by manufacturers and computer specialists of seven countries (the U.S.A. and six European countries) is a more flexible and powerful language than Fortran, though it is little used in America because of heavy investment and widespread use of the I.B.M. version. Both languages accommodate scientific needs, while Cobol, a business-oriented (*Co*mmon *b*usiness *o*riented *l*anguage) com-piler language, was developed in 1959 by a group of U.S. manufacturers and users. Cobol uses English words and terms, and also powerful commands, so that each command represents a lengthy sequence of machine instructions; it requires, however, a considerable part of computer time to translate the compiler language into machine language. In general, while Cobol is appropriate for business data processing, Fortran and Algol allow engineers and scientists to prepare their problems for computers. It must be noted that the more comprehensive the language, the more complex it becomes, e.g. Iverson's language.

The problem of a common computer language is at present receiving a great deal of attention. Today there are many computer 'high-level' languages, such as Cobol, Fortran or Algol, some of them very similar to others, some of them unique; some of them are available for several different computers, others available for one type of machine only. Some computer languages are suitable for specific problems, others for a wide range of applications. They are all similar to mathematical formulae or commercial jargon, containing alphabetic codes, mnemonics and even ordinary expressions in English. The object is thus to develop a standard programming language which would ease enormously the problem of communication between man and machine, i.e. to introduce a standard language with compiler programs available for all machines. Thus programs could then be interchanged between users, and libraries of programs could be established for the users of different systems for standard applications. Furthermore, users could then take advantage much more easily of other companies' systems or manufacturers' service bureaux. The burden of programming research would be considerably reduced. ·

There are a number of arguments advanced by both the manufacturers and users against a common computer language. Firstly, computers are very different in capacity and flexibility, so that compilers and languages have always been written for groups of computers of a given type. Hence, if compiler programs * were to be produced for a common lan-

---

* The compiler program bridges the gap between the language or 'source' program and machine or 'object' language; the computer can only act upon the latter, which consists of a number of sequences, usually long chains of zeros and ones.

guage they would probably be less efficient than those written for the language best suited to a particular machine.

Another argument used against the introduction of a common language is that the computer science dealing with computer languages and compiler programs is in its infancy, so that the development of a standard language would inhibit the evolution of this science. Finally, the opponents of the concept of a common language believe that the purpose of several high-level languages is to enable the user to program his problem in a form closely related to his own professional terminology.

In general, the difficulty lies in reconciling the ease of programming with the efficiency of solving a problem or carrying out an operation by means of a computer. Opinion is at present divided about the outcome of the struggle between the uni- and multi-language protagonists. But having said that, it is clear that there is a need for one 'ideal' or unique standard computer language. But the difficulties are enormous, since the requirements are most stringent. Such a language would have to be flexible but unambiguous, concise but precise, adaptable to all computers but governed by the characteristics of none; in addition, it should be easily read by all operations, while being optimum for all types of programs. While this task is most difficult to accomplish, the failure to do so is prodigiously expensive when one considers that there are in the U.S.A. 28 computer manufacturers with their own specifications and standards of hardware and software, while the enormous sums invested in hardware are nearly equal to those spent on software. Though the problem is enormous, the stakes are high, and various Government and private agencies in several countries are now engaged in battling with this tremendous impediment to further progress.

In the meantime, efforts are being made to develop a programming language specifically intended as an aid to software development. One of these, S.P.L. (Software Programming Language), is now being developed in the United Kingdom by C.E.I.R. Ltd., in association with the Ministry of Technology. S.P.L. is conceived as a full computer language similar in form to Fortran or Algol, but it is fundamentally different from those languages. Thus at present it is necessary to write translator programming for high-level languages in the specific computer machine code involving very many instructions. However, in the case of S.P.L., the language translator could be written in S.P.L. and the final translator produced via an S.P.L. translator; this is peculiar to the machine being used, but is itself relatively small and can be used for all other specialised translators. An important aspect of this development in the speed with which software written for one system can be transferred to another – a situation which arises when equipment is being updated; only about one man-year's work is expected to be required to provide a S.P.L. translator for any particular make of computer without any significant loss of performance in the software produced. The development of this and other aids may significantly reduce the delay in using new hardware systems and effect considerable improvement in the software position.

Conversational mode

The object is to make it possible for anyone with a problem to 'converse' with the computer without a specialist intermediary. In other words, the user communicates his problem to the computer and the latter replies to the user, advising him how to attack the problem and informing him of progress made.

Several means exist of feeding information into and extracting the results from the computer, but in practice the 'conversation' is conducted via special typewriters electrically connected to the machine. For instance, in business applications the user has access to all his company's files; he can extract required data that are kept up to date and are reliable, and interrogate the computer about the possible outcome of a given course of action. The machine compares various alternatives, searches its 'memory' and informs the user about the best business procedure.

This man–machine dialogue occurs most intensively with a program known as the Company Model. The object of this exercise is to store data about stocks, order, work in progress, cost and prices, etc., and then to produce trading accounts, cash analyses and balance sheets; the transition between the two functions is accompanied by the user's instructions to explore various possibilities and try out hunches. In order to use the big machines more effectively, it is necessary to arrange for 'multi-programming', i.e. the handling of several unrelated programs concurrently and shifting the attention of the computer constantly from one user to another according to their respective demands. An example of this type of machine is the pioneering project MAC at the Massachusetts Institute of Technology. This Multiple Access Computer enables a number of users to interrogate the machine virtually simultaneously, as noted later on in this chapter. It is worth noting that MAC also stands for 'machine-aided cognition', i.e. the computer assists the user in making effective decisions by means of this conversational mode.

The future for these conversational systems is exciting and full of promise. The necessary hardware already exists, but the software is still insufficient, i.e. there are not enough problem-solving programs available, nor indices for locating all stored programs, nor are there sufficient compilers and programming aids. Moreover, it is necessary to have a foolproof system for ensuring privacy * and inviolability of programs and data stored by a given user. On the other hand, the time-sharing arrangement is very economical, particularly since the programmers' productivity may be greatly increased by this arrangement, as shown, for example, in I.C.T.'s project MOP (Multiple On-line Programming).

The National Computing Centre in Manchester, England, is preparing the ground for a national computer grid, while in 1966 English Electric-Leo Marconi started building a computer which up to 200 people will be able to use at once. This could be the forerunner of a 'plug-in' computer, which subscribers could use by means of a telephone link. This was dramatically demonstrated in September 1966 when problems posed at a

* See 'Notes and Comments', *New Scientist*, 17 November 1966, p. 333.

lecture in Heriot-Watt College in Edinburgh were solved within seconds at the Computer Centre at Dartmouth, New Hampshire, U.S.A., by the use of telephone links. It is essential for the effective use of this time-sharing system to frame problems in a simple computer language and to have reliable data links. The evolution of a 'talking' computer would facilitate the operation enormously. Research has shown that it is possible to build a computer system which gives a spoken answer to a spoken question. Human speech is broken down into a digital form, while digital coding could, in turn, be used to produce tolerably human sounds. Recent progress in producing increased rapid-access storage capacity has made it possible to create large vocal memory banks whose output can be triggered to yield speech. The major problem of man–machine interface will probably be solved in the not too distant future.

THE FUTURE OF COMPUTERS

Apart from the lines of development already indicated, such as nanosecond machines, perceptrons, ideal programming language, etc., there are a number of topics now occupying the minds of researchers. Apart from such esoteric applications as the composition of music, plays, poems, love letters, there are more weighty tasks. There is the matter of man–machine dialogue or conversational mode, which would enable man to 'talk' to the machine and hence obtain immediate feedback, thus making 'conversation' possible. Another area is that of time-sharing, i.e. the use by many consumers by means of terminal consoles of a central computer or computer grid, like that envisaged by the Manchester National Computing Centre under the direction of Professor Gordon Black, or project MAC at the M.I.T., where Institute personnel can dial an I.B.M.-7094 computer from 40 different desks to store and retrieve information at any time during 24 hours; different users can, in effect, 'converse' with the computer in different languages nearly at the same time and use it in different ways.

Other spheres of present research activities are language translation and pattern recognition – both still in their infancy.

Difficulties in the former domain are due to the fact that present-day computers translate literally and not idiomatically, while the machine is incapable of perception or coping with ideas to recognise written characters or patterns except on a very limited basis. This field of activity is closely linked to recognition and synthesis of speech. The analysis or recognition is most difficult, since there are differences in pronunciations of the same word by individuals; on the other hand, computers have already been programmed to synthesise speech. Allied to these goals is the vast problem of information storage and retrieval, particularly in this age of information explosion, when over two million scientific articles are published every year and the amount of information is doubling every 15 years.

The greatest prize in the search for the ultimate is the creation of artificial intelligence akin to the human brain, including 'thinking'. The pioneers of this development are the father of cybernetics, Dr Norbert Wiener, the mathematicians von Neumann and Turing, Ross Ashby with his concept of homeostat, Minsky with his simulation of self-organising network, Grey Walter with his experiments in neurocybernetics, and Shannon with his theory of information. The work in this field has produced a welter of emotive protest and confusion, hence the term 'artificial intelligence' has been replaced by 'mechanical problem-solving'. The concept of thinking is, however, rather more difficult, since the term itself is hardly definable. The fact remains that present-day computers can manipulate numbers and symbols, and that programs exist which can simulate human processes of learning and crudely deal with abstract ideas. By probing into processes whereby humans learn, tackle puzzles, play games or make decisions, it is hoped eventually to design a machine capable of simulating human behaviour to an impressive extent.

PERCEPTRONS AND TURING MACHINES

The reasons for the limitations inherent in computers may be found by studying some characteristic features of the human

brain. Firstly, man's brain shows not only digital characteristics, in the transmission of electrical pulses, but also
analogical features, in that muscular contractions produce
changes in blood pressure. Secondly, although the brain has
about 10 000 times as many components as a large computer,
they occupy about $\frac{1}{100}$ of the volume; however, the nervous
centre functions much more slowly than a computer. Thirdly,
there is a great deal of interchangeability among parts of the
brain, and different regions can sometimes take over each
other's functions. Finally, a damaged brain can repair itself by
re-establishing new connections among neurons, as the
nervous cells do not appear to be connected according to a
rigorous wiring diagram like that of a computer. In effect, it
seems likely that most of the connections in the brain develop
at random, though some organisational features are 'deterministic' and subject to heredity.

The last aspect presents some difficulty, since it is hard to
understand how such a randomly connected system can learn.
To demonstrate the possible way in which a brain learns,
Professor F. Rosenblatt of Cornell University conceived, in
1958, an electronic model. The first 'perceptron' was constructed in 1959. It consists of three parts: a grid of 400
photocells, which respond to light stimuli; a group of 512
associator units, which have 40 random connections with the
photocells (it is impossible to predict in advance the pattern of
connections); and a response organ consisting of eight units
which receive signals from a given associator unit which, like
a neuron, transmits the signal if the latter is above a certain
threshold.

It is interesting to note that some associators can be destroyed without damage to its learning operation, since the
apparatus uses new paths among the remaining associators in
the same way as a damaged brain does. Thus the perceptron
can demonstrate some of the learning processes of randomly
connected systems. It can learn to recognise shapes in an
evolutionary way. For instance, if the photocell grid is shown
an illuminated shape, such as a letter or figure, it will respond
in a certain way. If it does not 'recognise' a slightly modified

shape, then it is shown the original again and again until it recognises the test sample. 'Recognition' is envisaged as an identical set of responses from the response organ, which is connected via the associator units with the photocell grid. Indeed, the perceptron could identify letters after about 40 exposures, even if the shape of the letter is somewhat altered or is situated in a different part of the visual field.

The first perceptron has been thoroughly studied and a variety of improved and modified units built. Dr Rosenblatt and co-workers have now constructed a model which is nearer in its organisation to the brain, since it combines partly random and partly deterministic organisation. This means, in effect, the introduction of restrictions in the presentation of shapes, such as deformation of letters in one particular way, in the same way that heredity imposes conditions upon the brain's learning. The perceptron then learns to perceive shapes much more quickly.

The future of brain-like computers may perhaps lie in the construction of perceptron-type machines containing a tremendous number of redundant parts and randomly connected parts with a small determinstic content. Such a computer would then be able to learn and repair itself by choosing alternative paths. The perceptron is only one of the several attempts towards devising systems which could serve as practically useful artificial intelligence devices, or to formalise psychological theories of human learning. In 1961, J. K. Hawkins published a survey of such self-organising systems. Some of these attempts result in the construction of machines which can simulate mental functions of the brain: playing chess or solving theorems in deductive systems. It is not considered likely that any computer at present can examine exhaustively all possible variant sequences in a game of chess for a given configuration of pieces. It is estimated that about 10^{120} chess games can be played. Hence if three choices could be examined by a computer in every millisecond, then the machine would probably take 10^{63} centuries to examine all the possibilities. This enormous load of computation is, however, greatly reduced by introducing selection procedures similar to the plausible hypotheses man uses when trying to solve a problem by trial and error. The computer works not by increasing the speed of operations but by using heuristic selection procedures, exploring possible avenues and selecting certain alternatives. In effect, such machines do very little arithmetic, but are capable of manipulating symbolic relations. All these efforts at simulating intelligent learning aim at ascertaining to what extent machines can be creative and ingenious.

Perceptrons and game-playing machines inevitably lead to the question, 'Do computers or computer-like machines really think?' It is nearly impossible to answer this, for so little is known about the processes of human thought. The late A. M. Turing, a brilliant English metamathematician, put the question in a form that is answerable in principle: 'Is it possible to distinguish between a given person and a given computer simply by communicating with them?' Turing proposed a game that could be played either with three people or with two people and a computer, so that the problem of distinguishability of people could be solved. The actual operation is performed by a question-and-answer method. Unfortunately, no computers are yet capable of successfully playing the Turing games.

Turing examined the problem of creative intelligence by conceiving an abstract automaton, called a Turing machine. A long tape is divided into squares each containing a symbol. The machine, which contains a collection of stored information, scans one square at a time and can read or change the symbol; it can also move the tape forward or backward by one square, while choosing its instructions. The machine has thus a definite cycle of operations. In general, it operates by deducing theorems from axioms, since from a defined set of symbols and rules it transforms the original set into another set on tape.

This work, which was done by Turing before 1939, gives an abstract characterisation of a digital computer and its logical organisation without a consideration of 'hardware'. It is essentially an abstract axiom system, and no one has ever built a Turing machine. The machine can theoretically be programmed to do any computation or logical operation that any other Turing machine can do, and a universal Turing machine could be programmed to imitate any other Turing machine. On the other hand, there are questions that a Turing machine cannot answer, because there are problems for which programmes cannot be devised. In effect, there are undecidable problems, similar to the Gödel theorem in arithmetic.

In any case, the problems of Turing machines are not normally applicable to industry. The point to be emphasised is that it is theoretically possible to effect crude imitations of the brain and create not merely computers but manufacturing plant which can operate truly automatically.

PROSPECTS AND POSSIBILITIES

It is clear from the above that it is theoretically possible to build machines which give a good imitation of intelligent thought. On the other hand, even if a supercomputer were available, with vast storage, phenomenal speed and immense flexibility, there would still remain the tremendous problem of programming the great machine. The complexity of the human brain could hardly be imitated by a computer and man submerged by machine. The veil covering the future is thick and impenetrable, though some tantalising glimpses are possible at infrequent intervals into the arena in which man and machine would meet for greatness or destruction. But whatever the future, computers already exist for sophisticated forms of automation. Before describing these applications and predicting future developments (Rose, 1967), it is necessary to consider the concept of feedback, which forms the basis of automation.

REFERENCES

ASHBURN, A. 1962. In *Ann. Am. Acad. pol. soc. Sci.*, **340**, 22.
BEER, S. 1964. In *Metra*, **3**, 1–12.
CLAPP, L. C., and YILMAS, H. 1965. Optical information processing. In COLBORN, R. (ed.) *Modern science and technology*. Van Nostrand, New York.
DIEBOLD, J. 1962. *Automation*. Vintage Books, New York.

DIEBOLD, J. 1965. *Focus on automation*, pp. 4–5 (U.K.). B.I.M. Publication.

FEUER, L. S. 1963. *The psychological and sociological origins of modern science*. Basic Books, London.

FOSTER, D. 1963. *Modern automation*, pp. 244–252. Pitman, London.

GÖDEL, K. 1931. In *Mh. Math. Phys.*, **38**, 173–198. [English translation: METZER, B. (ed.). 1962. *On formally undecided propositions of principia mathematica and related systems*. Oliver & Boyd, Edinburgh.]

LEITCH, W. R. 1966. In *Int. Mgmt*, **21**, 25–28.

MARCONI, G. 1932. In *Proc. roy. Inst.*, **27**, 509.

REINTJES, J. F. 1962. The intellectual foundations of automation. *Ann. Am. Acad. pol. soc. Sci.*, **340**.

ROSE, J. 1967. *Automation: its uses and consequences* (*C.S.P. 9*). Oliver & Boyd, Edinburgh.

SCHUH, J. F. 1965. *Principles of automation*, pp. 6 *et seq.* Cleaver-Hume Press, London.

WILLIAMS, W. T. 1962. Computers as botanists. *Proc. roy. Inst.*, **39**, 306.

WOOD, O. L., and FOX, H. L. 1964. Fluid computers. In COLBORN, R. (ed.) *Modern science and technology*. Van Nostrand, New York.

BIBLIOGRAPHY

BLOCK, H. 1962. The perceptron. *Rev. mod. Phys*, **34**, 123.

BOOTH, A. D. 1965. *Digital computers in action*. Pergamon Press, Oxford.

DODD, K. N. 1966. *Computers*. Pan Books, London.

FEIGENBAUM, E. A., and FELDMAN, J. (eds.) 1963. *Computers and thought*. McGraw-Hill, New York.

HOLLINGDALE, S. H., and TOOTILL, G. C. 1965. *Electronic computers*, Penguin Books, Harmondsworth, Middx.

MOSELEY, M. 1964. *Irascible genius, Charles Babbage*. Hutchinson, London.

NEUMANN J. VON, 1958. *The computer and the brain*. Yale Univ. Press, New Haven, Conn.

ROSENBLATT, F. 1961. *Principles of neurodynamics*. Spartan Books, New York.

THOMAS, S. 1965. *Computers*. Holt, Rinehart & Winston, New York.

WELBOURNE, D. 1965. *Analogue computing methods*. Pergamon Press, Oxford.

WIENER, N. 1961. *Cybernetics*. M.I.T. Press, and Wiley, New York.

1965. *Proceedings of the A.F.I.P.S. Conference*, Vol. 27, Part 1. Macmillan, London.

2. Feedback Control

'The coming decade will see an enormous increase in the use of feedback controls in industry, in the military services, in business operations and in situations which may involve all of these elements in our society.'
J. A. HRONES, The James Clayton Lecture, Institution of Mechanical Engineers, London, 1960.

HISTORICAL INTRODUCTION

In the beginnings of history man had to rely upon his own strength or that of domesticated animals to supply energy for doing work. Later on, he used levers and wheels to construct great engineering structures such as pyramids, aqueducts and highways. He then harnessed power from natural sources such as waterfalls and the wind for turning wheels and sailing ships. The steam-engine was, however, the first major attempt to harness *at will* useful power.

Early equipment and machines had mainly manual controls, but as man developed his propensity for building more sophisticated tools he also invented control systems of increasing complexity. The advent of automatic control did not really occur until James Watt made his great contributions to the development of the steam-engine in the latter part of the 18th century. The insatiable demand for coal to fuel the steam-engine, which made power available for work previously accomplished by human labour, brought about the invention of the speed governor – the first real automatic controller. The construction of this automatic aid was essential for the removal of the water from the coal mines, since the speed had to be controlled at widely fluctuating loads. Manual controls were ineffective for the purpose of accuracy of control and stability of operation. James Watt developed the fly-ball speed governor, which has since undergone many

alterations and improvements. However, the design of these
controls was based on empirical considerations and not on
scientific principles.

The explosive growth of steam-engines and the machines
they powered was not matched by an understanding of control problems. It was not till a century later that Clerk Maxwell
applied differential calculus to the design of a combined
engine–governor system and to the prediction of the behaviour
of this single-loop feedback control unit (Maxwell, 1868). This
problem of speed-control received renewed attention at the
turn of the 19th century owing to the rapid development of
power sources, particularly the steam turbine.

A different type of control, the position servo system, based
on feedback, was developed during the First World War by
N. Minorsky in order to maintain automatically a ship on a
prescribed course. This was accomplished by means of allowing a signal, which was the difference between the desired
course and actual course, to actuate a mechanism that continuously reset the ship's steering. Indeed, Minorsky's fundamental paper entitled *Directional stability of automatically
steered bodies* (Minorsky, 1922) laid the foundation for the
development of industrial control systems based on closed-
loop principles.

The important development of the position servomechanism
was followed by the pioneering work of researchers in the
laboratories of the Bell Telephone Company in the U.S.A.,
which resulted in the construction of feedback amplifiers in
telephone communications. This device was needed to amplify
the signal in order to compensate for loss in signal strength
with transmitted distance. One of the most important papers
published by Bell Telephone's research workers was that by
H. Nyquist on *Regeneration theory* (Nyquist, 1932), which
dealt with the stability of feedback control systems. The
importance of the Nyquist treatment in control design was not
recognised till the outbreak of the Second World War, during
which the development of sophisticated control systems,
particularly in military fields, made great strides. Feedback
control techniques have also proved most useful in business

operations, and even in the construction of economic models of our society in order to predict the response of the structure to economic forces. As far back as 1936 J. M. Keynes suggested in his great work on *The general theory of employment, interest and money* (Keynes, 1936) a simple model of this nature, while A. Tustin discussed the application of closed-loop dynamics to a modification of the model in his book *Mechanism of economic systems* (Tustin, 1954).

POSITIVE AND NEGATIVE FEEDBACK

The above control systems were based on the principle of feedback, i.e. a signal dependent upon the output signal is fed back to the input of the system in such a way that it affects its own value. The forward and feedback paths are combined to form a closed-loop system. The Watt steam-engine governor, which is generally regarded as the first of the deliberately contrived feedback mechanisms (Fig. 3), may serve as an example of a closed-loop system. The governor consists of weighted drums mounted on pivots, so that they are free to rise by centrifugal force as they revolve. As the speed of the engine increases, the arms rise and operate a valve which admits less power to the engine. In other words, the more the machine tends to exceed a given speed, the less it is supplied with energy to do so. The reverse is also true, i.e. more energy will be supplied to the engine if it does not reach a given speed. Hence a desired output is attained by self-regulation, and the system behaves like a homeostat, i.e. a control device for holding a variable between desired limits and operating against all kinds of disturbances. The schematic representation of this closed-loop system is shown in Fig. 3. The pilot valve and power piston serve to amplify the signal from the governor, since the force available at the governor is insufficient to actuate the throttle valve directly. The governor setting and engine speed are interdependent, so that the governor senses any deviation of the engine speed from a given setting.

The Watt governor is an example of negative feedback, since the governor senses the positive deviation between the desired homeostatic parameter, i.e. engine speed, and actual output of the machine; the feedback then counteracts this, *reducing* the deviation. Alternatively, a power-assisted brake mechanism constitutes an example of positive feedback, since it detects the small manual movements made and enlarges them till the force applied is capable of stopping a vehicle in motion, i.e. the action of the brakes is increased. Another example of positive feedback is a regenerative oscillator, where part of the output voltage is fed back to the input circuit in the correct phase (at the frequency of oscillator) to

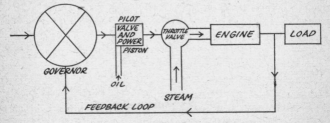

Fig. 3. *Closed-loop diagram of a steam-engine governor.*

further increase the output voltage. In other words, the function of the control mechanism which involves positive feedback is to *amplify* a measured deviation.

The applications of the principles of negative and positive feedback are by no means confined to inanimate matter. Living organisms display a wide variety of such mechanisms. Indeed, life is dependent on an incredible variety and number of interdependent feedbacks of both types. For instance, in the case of the digestive system in animals the flow of digestive juices is brought about by feedback using a combination of various mechanisms involving nerve impulses, hormones, and physical and chemical stimuli. The digestive feedback of the Pavlov dog, which salivated in response to an unnatural stimulus, e.g. sound, after having been subjected to conditioning experiments, is a vivid example of the operation of this principle. The rate of breathing, body temperature or the rate of heart beat and other vital processes rely on feedback. This phenomenon is not confined to elementary physiological phenomena, for even advanced behavioural features also involve a feedback mechanism, e.g. posture, which is controlled via muscle tonality and other bodily homeostats. When a man extends his arm to pick up an object, his brain directs his hand towards the object on the basis of a nerve signal obtained by visual comparison of the desired and actual position of the hand; similar considerations apply to feedback in a psychological context and even in the realm of economics, since in the view of cybernetics an economy of whatever size is homeostatic, including feedback controls that can be measured, so that the behaviour of the economy is to some extent predictable and controllable (see end of this section). It follows that simulation methods of operational research may produce a sensible model of an economy competent to deal with any real-life problems.

The problem of the 'psychological' feedback has received some attention. For instance, a possible cybernetic approach to the problem of memory, with its learning, selective storage and capacity to forget, was made by von Foerster in his *Quantum theory of memory* (von Foerster, 1950). His calculations led to a model which very closely resembles that of the human brain; in fact, von Foerster endeavoured to explain hallucinations and weird memories sometimes experienced by people. This model is rather remote from the 'memory' of present electronic computers, with their inelastic and unselective properties, since the von Foerster model contains the feedback feature by means of which a certain proportion of impressions of events is fed back into the memory's free spaces newly created by the process of forgetting. Hence the memory contains some impressions previously retained plus some more impressions fed back into the spaces created by the process of forgetting. In other words, this feedback is a learning process.

---

* 'Economic' feedback presents some interesting aspects. Tustin has applied the concept of feedback to the Keynesian

* The following section, which ends on p. 59, contains the relevant mathematical treatment in greater detail.

model of the economics of production and consumption (Tustin, 1953). In particular, he deduced the well-known Keynes result that investments equal savings. Tustin's approach was as follows: the total of all incomes (Y), which is spent in consuming things, is made up of money spent in producing things. The money spent in production may be divided into two classes: (i) that spent in producing goods which are consumed (P); (ii) that spent in producing capital goods, which is an investment (I). The money spent in consumption can be similarly divided in that spent in buying goods (C) and that saved (S). In this model, other effects such

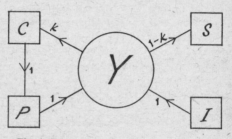

Fig. 4. *Economic mode.*

as stock-holdings are ignored, it being assumed that the level of consumption directly regulates production. Now, if the input to and output from the national income are to be in balance, then some feedback is necessary from consumption to production. The diagrammatic model is given in Fig. 4. The propensity to consume ($Y - C$) is a fraction k of Y, while savings are equal to $(1 - k)$, other factors being of unit value, as shown. The values of the feedback coefficient $1/(1 - k) = (Y/I)$ arises from the fact that the propensity to consume is fed back to Y, so that the influence from I to Y is not unity. It is worth noting that this coefficient is Keynes' investment multiplier, by means of which any increment of investment has to be multiplied in influencing income. The value of the coefficient may be found by considering a simple

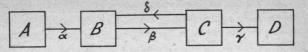

Fig. 5. *Single system with feedback.* (α, β, γ, δ *connect the systems.*)

system with feedback shown in Fig. 5. β is influenced not only by α derived from A but by feedback δ from C.

Hence

$$B = \alpha A + \delta C.$$

But

$$C = \beta B,$$

so that

$$B = \alpha A + \delta\beta B.$$

Rearranging, it is seen that

$$B/A = \alpha/(1 - \delta\beta)$$

or, if $k = \delta\beta$, then

$$B/A = \alpha/(1 - k).$$

It follows, that the effect of A on B has to be multiplied by $1/(1 - k)$. Transposing this reasoning to the Keynes' model, the influence of I on Y is now $1/(1 - k)$, starting with unity factors for P and C, i.e. $Y/I = 1/(1 - k)$. It may also be seen that, since savings S amount to $(1 - k)$ of Y,

$$I = Y(1 - k)$$

thus

$$I = S$$

which is the Keynes result that investment equal savings.

Tustin has produced more sophisticated models on the assumption that national economy is homeostatic and that it includes feedback controls.

INHERENT FEEDBACK

In the systems discussed so far, feedback is applied by means of a separate network. But there exist systems in which feedback is inherent in the system itself. An example of such a system is a transformer, which consists of a pair of coils wound around a core. It is found that the ratio of input and output voltages tends to be independent of the properties of the core. Furthermore, the greater the permeability of the core material, the more nearly are the properties of the transformer independent of those of the core. In other words, with a core of high permeability the difference between the applied signal (input ampere-turns) and the feedback signal (output ampere-turns) is small, while the properties of the transformer (ratio of input to output voltages) tend to be nearly independent of those of the core, as in amplifiers with negative feedback. Transductors, which are magnetic amplifiers, behave in a similar way.

A well-known example of a control system with inherent negative feedback is the equipment used for adding size to warp threads prior to weaving. This is achieved by passing the thread through a tank containing an aqueous solution or suspension of the solid, and then drying off the water. In order to deal with changes in temperature, viscosity, concentration, etc., which affect the amount of the solid added to the warp, it is only necessary to keep the volume of the solution or suspension in the tank constant and add solid material to the tank at the rate at which it should be removed by the warp. If the warp threads take up too much solid, then the concentration of the solution in the tank decreases until equilibrium is attained between the rates of addition and removal. The reverse applies if the take-up rate is too low, when the concentration will increase until the correct removal of size by the warp is taking place.

CLOSED- AND OPEN-LOOP SYSTEMS

Consider, for instance, a temperature control system, such as a thermostatically controlled water bath, as represented in Fig. 6. The object is to maintain a well-lagged bath of water at a constant temperature without altering the level of water. The temperature of the bath can be raised by an immersion heater connected to an a.c. supply through a variable autotransformer. Temperature control can be adjusted by varying the power supplied to the immersion heater as a function of the bath temperature. It is thus necessary to devise an input quantity, representing the constant temperature required, to

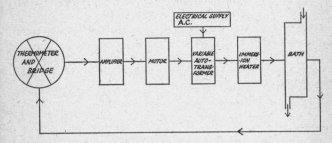

Fig. 6. *Closed-loop system.*

act as a reference with which the output quality, i.e. the temperature of the water at any given moment, can be compared. This is achieved by converting temperature changes into proportional electrical resistance changes by means of a resistance temperature, which forms one of the arms of the familiar Wheatstone bridge (Fig. 7), in which the adjacent

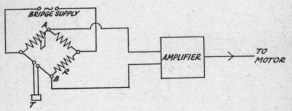

Fig. 7. *Control unit of Fig. 6.* ($T = $ *resistance thermometer immersed in bath.*)

arm (R) is a resistance equal to that of the thermometer at the required temperature; the remaining arms are two equal resistances comparable in value to others. When the temperature of the water bath is at the required value, no voltage difference is detectable across terminals AB by the bridge supply. However, if the temperature rises above the set temperature, a bridge imbalance results and the voltage difference is fed to an electronic amplifier, the output of which actuates a small motor; this drives the variable auto-transformer (Fig. 6), resulting in a reduction of power-input to the immersion heater. The reverse occurs during a temperature fall, which may be due to the removal of hot water and its replacement by cold, or to small radiation losses.

In the above example, the desired temperature is the reference input, while the actual temperature of the system is the controlled variable. The difference between the two is compared by the Wheatstone bridge, and the error signal (i.e. the voltage difference at *A* and *B*) is the actuating signal which is sent to the heating unit in order to correct the temperature. Thus two events occur in this scheme: (i) the controlled variable is *compared* with the reference input, and (ii) the resulting error signal, if any, *actuates* the control mechanism to change the output in order to minimise this error. Here one is dealing with a closed-loop system. Another example is the speed-control system of the centrifugal governor which subtracts the feedback signal from the reference input. Well-known examples are irons, refrigerators and household furnaces.

In an open-loop system there is no comparison between the reference input and controlled variable. Here, each setting of the input determines a fixed operating position for the control elements. For example, arrangements can be made to supply a fixed rate of heat to a house, the amount is preset from time to time to suit the external temperature. In this case the inside temperature (controlled variable) varies appreciably with the outside temperature. An alternative approach is to increase the temperature in the house, compare it with a desired value and use any difference between the two quantities to vary the supply of heat so as to reduce the difference. The former is an open-loop system, the latter example is a closed-loop system (Fig. 8). It is, of course, possible to obtain better control by using very expensive components, e.g. very effective insulation of the house. But, in general, the closed-loop system involves the use of relatively inexpensive components in order to obtain efficient control. Thus feedback in the closed-loop system enables continuous control to be exercised, whatever the external disturbances, while in open-loop systems – which do not involve feedback – this is most difficult and expensive to achieve.

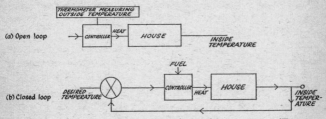

Fig. 8. *General open- and closed-loop systems.* (*Temperature control.*)

A simple example illustrating the difference between the two systems is the highly mechanised method of filling bottles with a liquid. The bottles pass on a conveyor belt under a filling nozzle in which there is a valve controlling the levels of the liquid in the bottles. A human operator watches the levels of the liquid in the bottles as they emerge, and removes those containing the wrong amount. This is an example of an open-loop system, where no actuating signal is sent back to the valve controlling the nozzle. Consider now an addition to this system, whereby the level of liquid in the filled bottles is checked by a mechanical device, which is capable of sending back continuously to the valve signals that can alter the volume of liquid added to each bottle. For instance, if insufficient liquid is added, the valve opens a little more, while overfilling brings about a corresponding partial closure of the valve. This shows in Fig. 9.

The disadvantages of the open-loop systems are as follows:

1. In order to achieve precise control it is necessary to know accurately the relation between a number of variables, e.g. in the case of temperature of a house it would be necessary to know the rate at which heat should be supplied for any given outside temperature.

2. An open-loop system cannot deal with disturbing factors other than those included in designing the system. For instance, if the rate of supply of heat is based only upon the value of the outside temperature, then the control will be upset by opening of windows. A closed-loop system can, in general, deal with all disturbing factors without an accurate

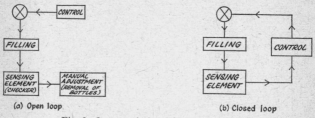

(a) Open loop   (b) Closed loop

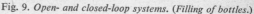

Fig. 9. *Open- and closed-loop systems.* (*Filling of bottles.*)

knowledge of the relation between the values of various factors and the control action to be exerted. It is, of course, necessary to know the correct sign of the feedback signal in order to obtain a suitable corrective action. For instance, in the case of thermostatic control of house temperature the rate of supply of heat must be increased if the house temperature falls.

Continuous and discontinuous controls

The sketch of the thermostatically controlled heating system shown in Figs. 6 and 7 is an example of a continuous type of control, since the controller output is always proportional to, or a continuous function of, the error. In our particular case, the error is the difference between the input voltage (corresponding to the reference temperature) and that developed across the resistance element of the thermometer, which forms the adjacent bridge arm (Fig. 7), and is proportional to the instantaneous water temperature; this error voltage is thus proportional to the temperature difference.

Consider now a water bath supplied with heat by an immersion heater. This supply is switched on and off by a contactor that is operated by a temperature-sensitive element immersed in the water. The contactor, which usually consists of a bimetallic strip that buckles when heated, can be made to open or close a pair of contacts; it can also be adjusted to do this at a certain temperature rise above that of the surroundings. Heat is supplied to the water until a certain temperature is reached, when the contact is broken owing to the buckling of the strip, the heat supply is then stopped and the temperature rise is arrested. When the temperature falls below the desired level, the strip straightens and the contact closes again, allowing heat to flow to the bath. In other words, once the required temperature level is attained, full power is switched on infrequently for short periods only. However, if hot water is withdrawn and replaced by cold water, power has to be switched on for longer periods and switched off for shorter intervals. Under all conditions the sensitivity of the control is increased if the difference between the upper and lower temperature limits (at which contacts open and close) is reduced, provided the bath is well lagged. In practice, however, sensitivity cannot be increased indefinitely by reducing this differential zone, owing to the presence of thermal lags in the equipment. When the period of one operating cycle is reduced to a value comparable with the time constant of the thermal lags, large temperature fluctuations take place and unstable operation results. This behaviour is similar to that of the Watt governor, where the mechanical mass inertia of the speed regulator causes sluggish response, this inertia being analogous to the thermal capacity in the temperature control.

The immersion heater described above is an example of a *discontinuous* control system. This type is simpler and coarser than the continuous variety, though various refinements are possible. On the other hand, the discontinuous systems are harder to analyse mathematically, because the controller action is generally non-linear, i.e. the controller output is not a continuous function of the error. Both systems, however, depend on the formation of error by feedback, which is then followed by an effort to reduce the error via a control mechanism.

PERFORMANCE OF FEEDBACK CONTROL SYSTEMS

The principle of feedback forms the basis of control technology, which is concerned with design, construction and operation of systems subjected to changing requirements. The system consists of a controlled plant (Fig. 10) which may have one or more outputs C, e.g. product, temperature velocity, pressure, position or flow. The behaviour of C as a

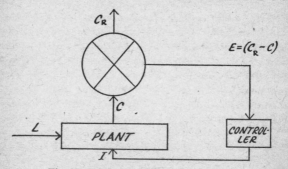

Fig. 10. *Simple feedback control system. C = output (controlled quantity); C_R = desired output; E = error; I = input; L = load or conditions.*

function of time is the result of changes of inputs I and the characteristics of the system. In the case of a continuous control system, which is linear, the outputs are linearly related to the input.

The values of the output of the plant must be known at any instant with an accuracy consistent with the desired result. Hence measuring instruments must be available, which have a speed of response that is fast relative to the speed of the plant. Moreover, they must not load and thus alter the behaviour of the plant. In order to satisfy this condition, the instruments must operate at low energy level relative to that of the plant. As regards the controller, power amplification is essential, since the manipulated quantity of output must be supplied at a high power level relative to the signal, which corresponds to the error in the controlled quantity or difference between the desired value of C_R and C itself. The plant, controller and regulator are interconnected to form a closed loop in order to feed back the measured behaviour of the output to manipulate an input to the plant. In this scheme the properties of the plant and controller are of equal importance in determining the overall system performance. It follows that it is vital to select a controller prior or during plant design.

Criteria of performance

A closed-loop system may exhibit three types of responses to a step change in an input. This is shown in Fig. 11, where E is the error and t is time. Course 1 represents an essentially non-oscillating response, when the response to a step change in input reaches the steady-state, associated with an error E_s at approximately the time t_s. In type 2, however, some oscillations are present, and the value of t_s is smaller than that of

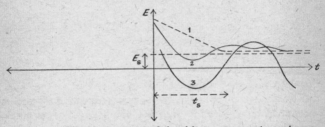

Fig. 11. *Responses of closed-loop systems to input changes.*

case 1, as the oscillating movement dies out quickly. This is not the case in type 3, where the oscillations have a considerable amplitude and require considerable time to die out, so that this system is too unstable for almost all applications. Another feature of type 3 is that the response oscillates about the zero steady-state position, and at equilibrium this error will be zero. In other words, a small error (type 3) and, to a smaller extent, a fast response (type 2) reduces the stability of operation.

At the design stage it is necessary to establish criteria of performance. The objectives of the control procedure are as follows:

1. The error, i.e. the difference between the desired value of output and its measured value, must be reduced to acceptable values during the whole operation of the plant, whatever the disturbances to the system. In other words, the steady-state error must be between acceptable limits.

2. The steady-state must be rapidly reached.

3. The system must not oscillate excessively and must be stable.

The above objectives of accuracy, speed of response and stability are necessary features of every control system. As regards the first characteristic, a control system must be accurate within specified limits, i.e. the system must be capable of reducing any error to a tolerable value. The limits are made as wide as possible, because the cost of a control system increases rapidly with requirements of increased accuracy. It is to be noted that no control system is able to maintain zero error at all times, since no corrective action, which arises out of an error, is possible. In practice, systems with a theoretical zero error do depart from ideality because of slight imperfections inherent in its components.

The speed of response is also of fundamental importance, since a control system must complete its reaction to a stimulus of some input, be it a reference change or a disturbance, within a reasonable period of time. If the response time to some input is far greater than the time interval between inputs, then the system may never 'catch up' and the demands will not be met, even if the required accuracy and stability are attainable.

As far as stability is concerned, this is an important requirement. A system is stable if the response to an input must reach and maintain some useful value within a reasonable period of time. An unstable system will, on the other hand, produce persistent oscillations of the output and may, even in the case of violent changes, drive it to some excessive value.

Ideally, a system should provide absolute accuracy, i.e. maintain zero error despite disturbances, respond instantaneously to a change in the input and be entirely stable. Such a system cannot, of course, be produced, and the control engineer must design a system so that the three general requirements are met as fully as possible. In practice, compromises are necessary between the various parameters, since requirements tend to be incompatible. Consider, for instance, the task of increasing the accuracy of the system. This may be accomplished by making the controller in the system more sensitive, so that it provides the same increment of correction for a reduced increment of error; the system can then respond to a smaller error. But then the stability of the controller will be adversely affected. The improvement in accuracy, if carried too far, may actually cause utter instability of the system. This may be seen by analysing a system where a slight error exists. If the controller is made very sensitive, then a corrective action will be initiated large enough to cause a response which will result in a greater error in the opposite direction. In other words, the system will 'overshoot' the proper value. The error will then cause to reduce the error, which is now greater in magnitude, so that a greater 'overshoot' will occur. The oscillations will thus increase until the amplitude is limited by the physical nature of the system, otherwise the system will destroy itself. It is clearly desirable to strike a compromise in this case between accuracy and stability.

While these requirements are common to all control systems, the actual values vary from one case to another. Thus, while for certain controlled-atmosphere chambers a steady-state error of $\pm 0 \cdot 1°$ F with a speed response of a few seconds and a very small overshoot are essential, the corresponding values for a centrally heated house of $\pm 2°$ F, 30 minutes and appreciable overshoot would be acceptable. The overall consideration is the relation between the requirements, which the system has to meet to fulfil its function, and system performance. The final design is usually a compromise between adequate stability, on the one hand, and lowest error and fastest response, on the other.

Self-adaptive control systems

It is clear that a controller designed for one set of conditions
may not be satisfactory for a quite different set of conditions.
For instance, in the course of time the characteristics of one
or more elements of the system may alter, thus affecting the
overall performance of the feedback mechanism. For example, corrosion in the pipes in a chemical plant may materi-
ally affect the rates of flow. Furthermore, the characteristics
themselves may vary widely over the range of conditions, e.g.
in an aircraft engine the characteristics vary over the normal

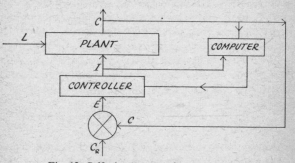

Fig. 12. *Self-adaptive control system.* I = *input;* C = *output* (*controlled quantity*); E = *error in controlled quantity;*
C_R = *desired value of controlled quantity;* L = *Load* (*set
of conditions*).

ranges of load and speed. It is, therefore, necessary in many
cases to design a system of control which is capable of changing its characteristics so as to maintain optimum performance
over a wide range of conditions. A model of such a self-
adaptive or self-optimising system is shown in Fig. 12. In this
simple model the controller characteristics are being changed
as the plant characteristics alter under the influence of L. The
computer 'instructs' the controller to alter its settings and thus
the plant input in response to information received at any
given instant about the output and input values. The information about the transfer characteristics must thus be known at
each instant of time (the transfer characteristics refer to the
relationships between changes in outputs and those of inputs

which cause them), since with this knowledge the new controller characteristics must be determined and the controller settings altered through the agency of the computer.

This development raises difficult problems of design, since plant characteristics may change gradually over a long period of time, or may undergo extensive changes in a short interval of time comparable to that of the actual speed of response of the controlled system; the enormous range between these two extremes must also be considered. On the other hand, the design engineer has to consider whether to obtain complete information on a sampling or continuous basis, particularly since digital computers are designed to operate on quantised rather than on continuous data. The sampling procedure is especially advantageous, because the interval between samples makes free time available on certain controller and computer installations, which can be used by other systems by incorporating an adequate switching arrangement. Hence a single controller can serve as a master installation for a number of different systems on a time-sharing basis.

The possibility of designing such a system is strong at present, although serious difficulties may arise due to the fact that very few systems are free from random inputs or disturbances. Hence, stochastic theory must be invoked to deal with this problem. (Stochastic phenomenon is a random one, which does not change its statistical properties with time, i.e. a series of events separated by random time intervals for which it is possible to specify the average interval and the ultimate pattern of these intervals.)

NON-LINEAR SYSTEMS

In the previous discussion one considered linear systems, i.e. those in which one or more outputs of any element of the system are proportional to the inputs of that element. In fact, few real systems are strictly linear over their entire range of operations. Nature has not made all physical relationships strictly linear. One states, for instance, that a spring is linear, meaning that the graph of force applied to the spring versus the resulting deflection is a straight line. In practice, one may find that the curve is slightly concave upwards, i.e. the spring rate is not a constant for all deflections, though in a narrow range the force–deflection curve is sufficiently close to a straight line to render the spring linear. The basic concept is that the behaviour of all physical systems in nature is inherently non-linear, though there may be regions over which a linear approximation is satisfactory.

Though some formal methods have been developed to deal with complex situations involving non-linearity, progress has been limited and only a few systems can be thus handled. On the other hand, analogue and digital computers can be used to handle non-linear system analysis, regardless, in most cases, of the complexity of the problems, even without the use of simplifying assumptions. Indeed, the non-linear element can actually be coupled to a computer if the latter is capable of operating in real-time. ('Real-time' refers to real-time data reduction, i.e. the processing of raw data or test data into useful intelligence by ordering and simplifying is done at the same speed as it is received from the primary instrumentation or sensors. On the other hand, 'on-line' data reduction refers to the processing of information as it is received by the computer system.) Moreover, non-linear differential equations, which form the mathematical basis of feedback control in non-linear systems, may sometimes be solved by the use of analogue computers. Some special cases may also be solved by specific techniques, such as those involving tabulated functions.

Another approach to this problem is by determining whether or not a non-linear control system is piecewise linear, i.e. its behaviour may be described by linear equations for particular regions of its operation. The procedure consists of solving the differential equation over a specific range, where the departure from linearity is small, and thus using the final values of the variables as the initial conditions of the following range. In general, linear theory can be used with valuable results in many instances, if the following conditions obtain: (a) the departures from linearity are small; (b) the changes in the system variables are limited around a specific operating point when performing the analysis; (*c*) a suitable linear model exists that is equivalent to the actual non-linear system.

Although in practice more systems are non-linear than linear, linear theory has been greatly successful in predicting performance and is proving a powerful means for advancing research into automatic control systems. Nevertheless, digital and analogue computers can deal with non-linear situations with remarkable efficiency and speed. Other procedures have also been used to handle these difficult problems, but, in general, the analysis of non-linear systems remains a largely unknown territory.

TRANSFER CHARACTERISTICS

Mention has already been made of transfer characteristics, which represent relationships existing between changes in outputs of a system and the changes in the inputs that cause them. The knowledge of these characteristics is essential for the optimisation of the design of a control system, since this enables one to predict in some measure the dynamic response to any disturbance.

The information about these characteristics is obtained by the following procedures: (*a*) calculations based upon previously determined physical laws; (*b*) measurement of output changes due to known input changes; (*c*) a combination of (*a*) and (*b*).

To compute or measure system characteristics four types of inputs are frequently used:

1. A pulse change in an input (Fig. 13).

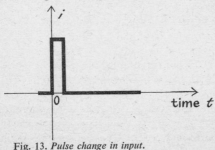

Fig. 13. *Pulse change in input.*

2. A step change in an input (Fig. 14). The output is increased as a function of time and the result is termed the 'indicial response' or 'step response'.

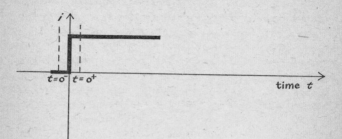

Fig. 14. *Step change in input.*

3. A sinusoidal input (Fig. 15). The input is maintained constant and at any given frequency ω, amplitude c_a and phase angle ϕ of the output are measured after the initial transients disappear. This is repeated several times with various values of ω at the same amplitude i_a.

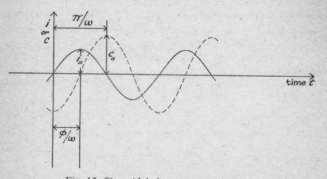

Fig. 15. *Sinusoidal change in input (solid line) i and output (broken line) c. (c_a or i_a = amplitude; ω = frequency; ϕ = phase angle.)*

4. A random input (Fig. 16).

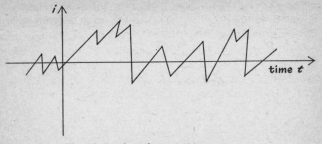

Fig. 16. *Random change in input.*

The dynamic behaviour of the systems is formally described by differential equations that relate changes in outputs to those of inputs; these relations are known as transfer functions of the system (see equations (2.1) to (2.8)).

As far as sound design is concerned, this problem of transfer characteristics must be viewed against the nature of the system. If the nature of the system is well known, a mathematical model can be constructed which describes the actual system behaviour; the equation relevant to this model, usually linear differential equations, can then be solved by various techniques available. However, if the nature of the system is not known, then the mathematical equations must be set up by measuring the output responses to input changes – a difficult and sometimes intractable problem.

SYSTEM REPRESENTATION

The mathematical relationships of parts of the control systems are usually represented by block diagrams. These diagrams, which indicate the actual processes taking place, may be combined to give an overall block diagram for an entire system.

Consider, for instance, a control element, which receives an input (i) signal. Fig. 17 shows the block diagram of the physical system C, where c is the controlled variable, which is the output of the system C, and $f_1(p)$ represents the operation of the system C. The quantity $f_1(p)$, which is given by the relation $f_1(p) = c/i$, could in principle be obtained by writing down the mathematical equations describing the operations of each component between i and c and then combining these individual equations algebraically to obtain the overall relation between i and c. This procedure is cumbersome for all but the simplest systems of the interaction of various components.

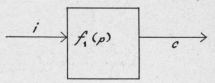

Fig. 17. *Block diagram.*

The diagrammatic method is, however, to be preferred, since the combination of the block diagrams for each component yields the desired representation for $f_1(p)$, while the visual representation of the system gives a better understanding.

Returning to the block diagram in Fig. 17, it is to be noted that the output could be fed directly into a unit, which can compare it with a reference input; this system is known as a unity-feedback. This unit, usually represented by a circle, is a symbol corresponding to a summing operation (Fig. 18). The

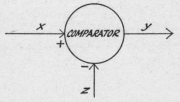

Fig. 18. *Block diagram of a comparator.*

arrowheads pointing towards the circle are input quantities, while those pointing away refer to output quantities; the sign at each input arrowhead shows whether the quantity is to be added ($+$) or subtracted ($-$). In the general case (Fig. 18) the actuating signal y (the signal arising from the comparator) is given by the difference ($x - z$). For instance, in a speed-control system with a centrifugal governor the actual speed, which is to be controlled, is continually compared with a desired value, and the error found then actuates the control elements. It is clear that it is possible to represent any linear

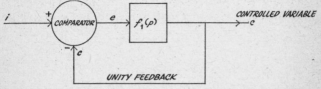

Fig. 19. *Block diagram of a feedback control system (unity feedback).*

mathematical expression by boxes (multiplication), and circles (summation) in a block diagram (Fig. 19, which is a combination of Figs. 17 and 18). The diagram in Fig. 19 shows pictorially why this system is of a closed-loop type (e is an actuating signal, equivalent to y of Fig. 18).

This system could be extended by including an element which converts the form of resulting output (controlled variable) into a form that is suitable for the comparator, e.g. the conversion of controlled temperature in a thermostatic system into a proportional force or position. The resulting closed-loop system is shown in Fig. 20. Here a signal e_2

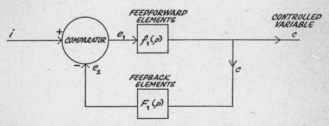

Fig. 20. *Forward and feedback networks.*

dependent upon the output signal c is fed back to the input in such a way as to affect i. This closed-loop system is seen to be composed of a forward and backfeed network. It is worth noting that feedback control systems fall into two main types: (i) regulators in which a reference input, though adjustable, is held constant for considerable periods of time, e.g. most temperature controllers or speed regulators; (ii) servomechanisms in which the controlled variable is a mechanical position, e.g. the angular position of a shaft, and control is on the basis of an error signal.

Effects of positive and negative feedback

There are two types of feedback: positive and negative. If the amplification of the system is increased by the effect of the feedback, then positive feedback results; negative feedback occurs if the amplification is reduced. A system may have positive feedback under some conditions and negative feedback in others. Furthermore, if the amplification of the forward network in a negative feedback is large (i.e. the absolute value of $f_1(p)$ is much larger than unity), then the properties of the system are determined almost entirely by those of the feedback network. The special properties of a negative feedback system are due to the tendency of the system to operate in such a way that the effective input to the system is small; the input and feedback signals are of opposite sign and approximately the same magnitude.

Two effects arise in negative feedback systems as the result of the above properties:

1. Since the properties of the system are determined almost entirely by those of the feedback network and are largely independent of those of the forward network, external disturbing effects can be reduced and stability enhanced. For instance, in an electronic amplifier the feedback network can consist entirely of passive components, the properties of which remain fairly constant, so that the behaviour of this amplifier is independent of main voltage changes; for hydraulic devices, for example, the effects of viscosity or temperature can also be minimised by choosing appropriate components. Moreover, if the amplification of an electronic amplifier changes with frequency of the input signal, then the output signal is a distorted version of the input signal. Indeed, it may be shown

that the effect of the disturbing influences may be made very small, since it is given by the factor $1/[1 + f_1(p)F_1(p)]^2$. It must be added, however, that this desirable effect is obtained at the expense of a large reduction in the amplification of the system.

2. Negative feedback tends to reduce to a small value the effective input to a system, the input and feedback signals being of opposite phase and approximately equal magnitude. Hence the output signal tends to be an exact replica of the input signal. Thus in an electronic amplifier the waveform of the output signal resembles that of the input signal. This similarity is increased by increasing the amplification of the forward network. This property of a negative feedback system is sometimes used to interchange cause and effect in a physical

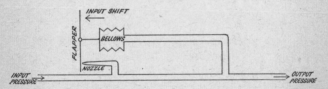

Fig. 21. *Negative feedback in a pneumatic system.* (*Flapper nozzle amplifier.*)

device. Consider, for instance, a pneumatic system for producing a pressure proportional to an applied mechanical shift (Fig. 21) contrary to the usual case of producing by bellows a displacement proportional to an applied pressure. The object may be achieved by using the difference between the applied shift and that of the bellows as the input to a high-gain pneumatic amplifier. In our pneumatic system there is no airflow through the nozzle, when the flapper of the flapper-nozzle amplifier is just contacting the nozzle; the output pressure is then equal to the input pressure. When the flapper is well away from the nozzle, the output pressure is very small owing to the large airflow. Between these two extremes, when the airflow is restricted, the distance between the flapper and nozzle can be made very small (about 0·001 in) and the force required to move the flapper may also be small by using a nozzle of a small area and causing the flapper to move in a plane across the nozzle. It is thus seen that the pressure output, which is also the desired one, from this amplifying device is fed back as the pressure causing the displacement of the bellows. Since the latter is proportional to the output pressure, a pressure is obtained that is proportional to the applied displacement, provided that the displacement of the bellows exactly cancels out the movement, at the nozzle, produced by the input signal.

* STABILITY OF FEEDBACK CONTROL SYSTEMS

A physical system is said to be stable when disturbed from its equilibrium condition, it ultimately returns to that condition. On the other hand, a system is unstable if the initial disturbance from the equilibrium condition increased indefinitely with time.

Control systems based on the feedback principle had been designed by semi-empirical procedures before the theory was formulated or understood. The 'fan-tail' used to keep the sails of a windmill pointing into the wind, or Watt's centrifugal steam-engine governor are examples of such development. However, these devices were improperly designed closed-loop systems, hence their instability. Thus the steam-engine governor would become unstable at times and the engine speed would fluctuate rhythmically, contrary to the then held beliefs.

The instability of these systems were not understood till H. S. Black in the U.S.A. developed valve amplifiers by using negative feedback. There appeared to be a discrepancy between theoretical predictions and the actual behaviour of these amplifiers. However, the classic paper by H. Nyquist of the Bell Telephone Company in 1932 (loc. cit.) elucidated this phenomenon and laid the mathematical foundation of the theory of stability of closed-loop systems, which is directly applicable to automatic controls, since the latter are essentially

* This section, which ends on p. 86, contains the relevant mathematical treatment in greater detail.

closed-loop systems capable of sustaining oscillations under certain conditions.

In order to evaluate the stability factors, it is necessary to consider the concept of transfer functions. These functions represent the relation between the input (i) and output (c) quantities for any physical system. Thus the transfer function for the simple system for which the input and output i and c respectively is given by equation

$$f_1(p) = c/i. \qquad (2.1)$$

Consider, for example, a simple electrical circuit with pure resistances (Fig. 22), which can also be represented by Fig. 19,

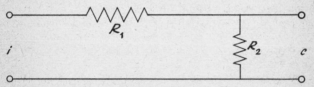

Fig. 22. *Simple electrical circuit.*

since one terminal is common to the input and output and for which the relation between the input voltage (V_i) and open-circuit output voltage (V_c) is given by

$$c/i = R_2/(R_1 + R_2) \qquad (2.2)$$

this relation being independent of the way in which the input voltage varies with time. However, this type of circuit with pure resistances does not exist in practice, since some capacitance and inductance are always present, and the ratio V_c/V_i depends upon the nature of the input signal. Hence the properties of the circuit must be expressed by a differential equation incorporating the resistance R, capacitance C and inductance L, i.e.

$$LC(\mathrm{d}^2c/\mathrm{d}t^2) + RC(\mathrm{d}c/\mathrm{d}t) + c = RC(\mathrm{d}i/\mathrm{d}t). \qquad (2.3)$$

This is a differential equation in which only the first power of i and c or their derivatives are involved, i.e. it is a linear differential equation, which can also be written in the form

$$c/i = RCp/(LCp^2 + RCp + 1) \qquad (2.4)$$

where p is the differential operator $(\mathrm{d}/\mathrm{d}t)$. Finally, the numerator and denominator of the right-hand side of the equation can be expressed as function of p, so that

$$c/i = f_1(p) = f_3(p)/f_2(p). \tag{2.5}$$

This function completely describes the properties of a system for which the equations are linear differential equations. Although in practice no system is perfectly linear, it is found that it behaves so over a limited range of values of the dependent variables, or if certain other assumptions are made. Furthermore, for complex systems where quite complicated differential equations obtain, transfer functions could be determined by the use of Laplace transforms or Heaviside's operational calculus; the reverse is also true, i.e. the determination of the properties of systems from their transfer function by the use of these mathematical devices.

The transfer function for a closed-loop system (Fig. 20) is found by noting that

$$c/e_2 = f_1(p) \quad \text{and} \quad e_2 = i - cF_1(p).$$

Hence $\qquad c/i = f_1(p)/[1 + f_1(p)F_1(p)]. \tag{2.6}$

This system has negative feedback if $f_1(p)F_1(p)$ is positive, since then the amplification of the system with feedback is less than that without feedback; positive feedback results when $f_1(p)F_1(p)$ is negative.

It may be seen from equation (2.6) that if $|f_1(p)| \to \infty$, the ratio c/i tends to unity, so that the output of the system tends to follow exactly any variations of input. Ideally, c/i should be unity; approximately ideal conditions could obtain if $|f_1(p)|$ is large. If the input signal is sinusoidal (Fig. 15), then the output c may follow the input i in an approximate manner. But if a step-function signal is involved (Fig. 14), then the input signal contains some dependent variables (frequencies, in the case of electrical circuits) for which $|f_1(p)|$ is not large, so that an error results between i and c. A system involving electrical circuits, e.g. an amplifier, will behave as a negative feedback only if the signal to be subtracted from the input signal is about the same phase as the input signal. On the other hand, if $f_1(p)$ is such that at some frequency e_2 and i are effectively added, then positive feedback results and

$$c/i = f_1(p)/[1 - |f_1(p)|]. \qquad (2.7)$$

Hence if $\qquad |f_1(p)| \geqslant 1$

the amplification tends to infinity. Thus, any chance variation in input will give a finite output c, and the system will oscillate at the frequencies at which input and feedback signals are added together. This instability must, of course, be avoided.

The system shown in Fig. 19 can also be represented by Fig. 23, so that $f_1(p) = c/e$, *an open-loop transfer function*, repre-

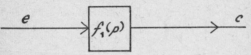

Fig. 23. *Representative of Fig. 19.*

senting the relation between the output signal c and error e. It is seen that this function is a part of the closed-loop transfer function (equation (2.6)).

It is necessary to stress the fact that it is possible to predict the behaviour of a closed-loop system from a knowledge of an open-loop transfer system, since the corresponding transfer functions are intimately related. In practice, the open-loop properties of a system can be measured by breaking the loop at any point and then feeding in an input signal and measuring the output signal at this point.

The closed-loop transfer function may be represented by

$$c/i = f_1(p)/[1 + f_1(p)]$$
$$= f_3(p)/[f_2(p) + f_3(p)] \qquad (2.8)$$

since $f_1(p) = f_3(p)/f_2(p)$, as given by equation (2.5). It may be shown that if any of the poles, which may be real or complex, of this transfer function, i.e. any of the roots of the equation

$$f_2(p) + f_3(p) = 0$$

have a positive real part, the system is unstable.

Table 5 shows the behaviour of the disturbances as given by

the value of the transient term. If a system is disturbed, then to each real pole p_r there corresponds a transient term $B_r e^{p_r t}$, where t is time.

Table 5. *Real poles.*

Value of pole	Value of transient term
Positive	Increases indefinitely
Negative and small	Decays slowly
Negative and large	Decays exponentially with time

The behaviour of complex poles, which exist in conjugate pairs $p = a \pm jb$, is shown in Table 6 (each pair represent oscillations of frequency $b/2\pi$, the amplitude being propor-

Table 6. *Complex poles.*

Value of a	Amplitude of disturbance	Damping of system
$a > 0$	Increases indefinitely	Negative damping
$a = 0$ (purely imaginary poles)	Simple harmonic motion of fixed amplitude	Undamped
$a < 0$	Decays with time	Positive damping (the greater $|a|$, the greater the damping)

tional to e^{at}). It is evident that greater stability will result if the real pole is large and negative, or when the term a in the complex pole is large and negative; in both cases the system is damped and thus ceases to be oscillatory and unstable.

There are three criteria of stability of closed-loop systems (electronic amplifiers are considered here as examples, but similar consideration will apply to other systems).

1. *Comparison with open-loop systems.* If the amplification A and phase shift θ of the open-loop network of an amplifier are studied in relation to the frequency of oscillation, then it is found that the system is unstable if $A \geqslant 1$ at $\theta = 180°$; the greater the actual amplification (in decibels) than 1 at $\theta = 180°$ (this is also known as the gain margin), the greater the stability, since the damping is greater. A gain margin of about 10 dB is generally satisfactory.

It should be noted that a system is undamped if the closed-loop transfer function is equal to -1 ($A = 1$; $\theta = 180°$); any increase of gain will make this system unstable.

2. *Routh–Hurwitz criteria*. These criteria are cumbersome to apply, particularly since the form of the transfer function has to be known exactly. Furthermore, they do not determine *the degree* of stability. The method consists of analysing the poles of the transfer function and applying algebraic criteria to determine whether or not the poles have negative real parts.

3. *Nyquist criteria*. This method involves frequency-response loci, i.e. the path traced out on an Argand diagram

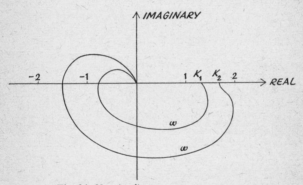

Fig. 24. *Nyquist diagram.*

(plot of imaginary versus real parts of the transfer function relating to the response of a system to a sinusoidal input signal for which the angular frequency is ω) by the point P_ω corresponding to a given value of ω. It may be shown that if this Nyquist plot, when locus is traversed from $\omega = 0$ to $\omega = \infty$, has the point $(-1, 0)$ on its left-hand side and the locus is turning about $(-1, 0)$ anti-clockwise, then the system is stable; if it passes through the point $(-1, 0)$, then the system is marginally stable, i.e. the system is undamped. It must also be noted that the position of the loci varies with open-loop gain, i.e. the open-loop amplification A at zero frequency is unity (Fig. 24). The degree of damping, i.e.

stability of the closed-loop system, is indicated by the close-
ness of the locus to point $(-1, 0)$. In practice, the resonance
ratio, i.e. the ratio of closed-loop amplification at resonance
to that at zero frequency, of about $1\cdot3$ is satisfactory.

GENERAL BEHAVIOUR OF FEEDBACK SYSTEMS

In general, actual systems do not behave ideally, i.e. output
does not follow exactly any variations of input. This relation
between the two quantities is obtained by solving equations
(2.5) or (2.8). The solution is the sum of two parts representing
(i) a steady-state response of the system to a given input
signal, and (ii) a transient part corresponding to the response
of the system when disturbed by the application of an input
signal; the latter part mainly depends on the properties of the
system and, to some extent, on the nature of the input signal.

A satisfactory performance of a system requires the following conditions to be satisfied: (a) the amplitude of these terms
shall decrease with time; (b) duration of the transient terms
shall be as short as possible; (c) the output shall follow input as
rapidly as possible. For an amplifying electronic system, for
example, conditions (b) and (c) will be satisfied provided the
natural frequency of the system is as high as possible, while
condition (a) requires that the poles of the closed-loop function shall be positive (condition (b) is also met if these poles
are large). Under these conditions damping is large. But then,
the time of response is increased and the frequency of the
transient oscillations is reduced. Furthermore, conditions (b)
and (c) require that the bandwidth (i.e. frequency range
$(0 - \omega_{\frac{1}{2}})$, where $\omega_{\frac{1}{2}}$ is the angular frequency at which the
amplification is reduced to one-half of its value at zero fre-
quency) be as large as possible.

In general, good performance is obtained when the natural
frequency of the system is high and there is adequate damping.
The latter has already been discussed in connection with
Nyquist diagrams. The former is related to the open-loop gain
(this is the open-loop amplification at zero frequency); the

greater the gain, the higher the natural frequency, so that steady-state errors of the system are small. But an increase of the gain also leads to instability for a given damping. Hence, in practice, a compromise is struck and the system is designed to give a gain, which could ensure some stability and steady-state performance.

It is interesting to consider an ordinary valve amplifier, which is virtually an open-loop control system, since its output is entirely dependent on the characteristics of its components. As a result, any distortions, drifts, variations of power supplies or spurious noise are amplified at the output. The problem consists, therefore, of introducing into the system an element of feedback in order to reduce these undesirable effects.

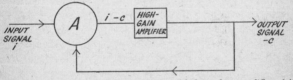

Fig. 25. *Closed-loop scheme of the valve amplifier.* (*A is equivalent to error-detector in control systems.*)

Consider, for instance, that the output and input terminals of the valve are connected in series and that the input and output signals are in exact anti-phase, i.e. a negative feedback loop is closed round the amplifier (Fig. 25); the internal gain of the amplifier is very high, e.g. 10^6.

However, the above leads to an amplifier with an overall (measured) gain of unity, though changes in values of the supply voltage or component characteristics within reasonable limits will hardly affect this gain. In other words, this is an automatic control system with a high speed of operation, but not an amplifier in the usual sense. But, if the input signal is constant in frequency and amplitude and if the internal gain is now reduced from 10^6 to 10^5, then the output signal fed back is reduced. As a result, the difference $(i - c)$ between the input signal, which is kept constant, and output signal fed back increases, while the overall gain is still nearly unity.

(For a higher gain, say 10^{12}, the opposite is true, and 'error' signal tends to very small values for full corrective action.) In this arrangement any tendency of the output amplitude to fall is immediately corrected, since the net signal at the amplifier input ($i - c$) increases and immediately counteracts the amplitude change. In general, any tendency of the output signal to deviate from its desirable value because of drift and variations within the amplifier is immediately corrected by the 'error' signal at the input terminal. Thus, in this type of valve 'amplifier' with unity gain, the internal or output impedance is lowered, i.e. the behaviour of the valve is nearly independent of the output loading, and the system has an inherent resistance to output amplitude variation caused by output loading. It is worth noting that in an amplifier without feedback this is not true, because of high internal impedance, and variations in the output loading result in variations of output amplitude.

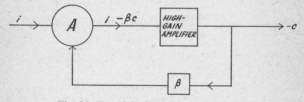

Fig. 26. *Partial feedback of output.*

It is clear from the above that the feedback of all the output into the input confers a high degree of stability upon the amplifier, while reducing the overall gain to a negligible value. If only a small part of the output is fed back, the stability is slightly reduced but the overall gain is increased. For instance, if the internal gain is 10^6 and the fraction fed back is 1% of the output, then the overall gain will be nearly 100; if the fraction is 0·1%, then the gain is nearly 1000. In both these cases the amplifier is quite stable and the output impedance much reduced (the 'error' signals are then given by $i - \beta c$ where β is the above fraction). In general, for an amplifier with high internal gain the overall (increased) gain is nearly equal to the reciprocal of β (Fig. 26). The gain is still nearly constant and the output impedance less reduced than before. A control system is, however, similar to a unity-gain amplifier, where all the output is fed back to the input and the distortion is slight.

A rigorous and more detailed treatment of the problem of stability is to be found in the following books:

DE BARR, A. E. 1962. *Automatic control*, Chapter 4. Chapman & Hall, London.

HARDIE, A. M. 1964. *Elements of feedback and control*, Chapter 6. Oxford University Press, London.

HARRISON, H. L. and BOLLINGER, J. G. 1963. *Automatic controls*, Chapters 9–14. International Textbook Company, Scranton, Pa.

RAVEN, F. H. 1961. *Automatic control engineering*. McGraw-Hill, New York.

These books are also concerned with feedback problems.

REFERENCES

FOERSTER, H. VON 1950. In *Transactions of the Sixth American Conference on Cybernetics*. Josiah Macy Jr. Foundation, New York.

KEYNES, J. M. 1936. *The general theory of employment, interest and money*. Macmillan, London.

MAXWELL, J. C. 1868. On governors. *Proc. roy Soc.*, **16**, 270.

MINORSKY, N. 1922. Directional stability of automatically steered bodies. *J. Am. Soc. nav. Engrs*, **34**, 280.

NYQUIST, H. 1932. Regeneration theory. *Bell Syst. tech. J.*, **11**, 126.

TUSTIN, A. 1953. *The mechanism of economic systems*. Heinemann, London.

TUSTIN, A. 1954. *Mechanism of economic systems*. Harvard Univ. Press, Cambridge, Mass.

3. Automatic Control

'We are now only the thirteenth richest nation in the world, in terms of wealth per head. It's going to be difficult enough even to hold that position. Without automation it will be impossible.'
SIR LEON BAGRIT, Chairman, Elliott-Automation

INTRODUCTION

Automatic control plays an ever-increasing role in our modern technological society, the devices ranging from the 'automatic' washing machines to complex systems controlling the movements of interplanetary vehicles. These automatic controls include a wide range of equipment, all of which is based on the principle that an output quantity (temperature, voltage, speed, etc.) is monitored with subsequent error-actuation of a controller, this operation being independent of a human operator. Any equipment which performs the same function as a continuously employed human operator may be termed an automatic control. This control may be called upon to perform various duties. For instance, a regulator type of control relates to a system wherein an output quantity to be controlled has to remain constant and the input has a fixed reference value, e.g. thermostats, engine governors or stabilised power units. On the other hand, the output quantity may have to follow continuous variations of input quantities, ranging from slow cyclic changes to sudden jumps.

It is worth noting that there are 'automatic' systems which are not strictly *automatic control* systems. For instance, a system may be automatic in one respect, but may require human control in another, e.g. in the Automatic Train Control a signal, actuated by a dangerous condition, sounds an alarm in the driver's cabin; the driver then applies his brakes and stops the train. In a servo system a human operator injects the

input signal into a system, so that a suitable output is produced via an error-actuated controller. The duty of the
operator is to indicate the output requirements on an input
scale without any monitoring duties. If the operator's function
were to be taken over by a suitable device, such as a special
motor-driven cam, then this servo system would become a
truly automatic control.

Historical notes

The industrial civilisation rests on the utilisation of energy.
While early man had to rely on his own strength or those of
domesticated animals, supplemented later on by mechanical
devices such as levers and wheels, the first breakthrough
occurred with the intelligent use of natural sources. Man then
used waterfalls to turn his wheels and wind to sail his vessels,
but he could not harness their useful power at will. The
invention of the steam-engine, however, provided man with a
source of energy that he could control. The object was then to
design machines which could use power to serve the purposes
of man and which could be made independent of human
operators even when performing functions that are beyond the
physical abilities of man to duplicate. To achieve this, man
had to develop his engineering capabilities and delve deeply
into the philosophy of automation. In the workings of his own
body, man had examples of sophisticated control systems far
beyond anything that he could design or build. The pioneering
work by Norbert Wiener (N. Wiener, 1948) on neurological
phenomena and control systems in the human body paved the
way to the development of complex automatic systems by
using cybernetics concepts.

The term 'cybernetics', which means the art of steermanship,
was coined by Wiener to cover the science of control and
communication.* It includes human and robot cybernetics;
the former is concerned with the study of the workings of the

* The Greek word '*Kubernetes*' gave rise to the Latin '*gubernator*', the
French '*governeur*', the English '*governor*' and Spanish '*gobernator*'.
Wiener was the first to point out the links between cybernetics and other
branches of science, particularly probability calculus and signalling
theory.

human mind, the latter with the study of electronic computers and automata. Since the essence of advanced automation is the 'robot brain' in control systems, whereby an attempt is made to imitate the human nervous system, it is clear that it is important to understand the workings of the human brain. A few examples may illustrate this connection.

Consider, for example, the human or animal reflex actions. An animal will withdraw any part of its body when it is confronted by an act likely to result in pain or injury. Man will remove his finger when it touches a hot surface, or close his eyes when faced by a sudden glare or attack upon them. This nervous reflex action is well developed in animals and man, and no thinking is involved. Some of these reflexes may be imparted to animals, such as in the case of Pavlov's dogs, which were made to salivate at the sound of bells. In the inanimate world the parallel systems are the immediate-reaction devices, such as centrifugal governors on steam-engines or lavatory ball-cocks, when a disturbing reaction is immediately followed by a counter-effect. This mode of automatic action is, however, far removed from complex automated system needed in our modern industry.

The above reflex actions are examples of an elementary corrective control. A more sophisticated control is that which involves the more developed parts of the brain – a 'thinking' operation that is equivalent to a 'considered know-how'. The controller (man) must first be able to diagnose a failure in some external system, on the basis of some process-target present in his memory, and then make a decision, which takes into consideration the controller's past experience, his mental skills in understanding how the given process works and in knowing the capability of the system to be controlled. The decision is made on the basis of the 'process know-how', which consists of four main parts:

1. Physical, which includes the controller's past experience in handling the process under conditions.

2. Symbolic, i.e. representation of (1) by mathematical formulae or graphical flow-sheets.

3. Analytical, i.e. sorting out the facts.

4. Synthesis of the above parts under the overall umbrella of logic, which is defined as 'the science of reasoning'.

The combination of diagnosis, memory and know-how is termed 'process thinking', which gives rise to a corrective action in the event of a system failing in some way to perform satisfactorily. The term 'thinking' refers to the ability of the controller to use mental functions in combination with facts stored in his memory and in accordance with logical rules to respond to an input of information; the actual 'feedback' part of this procedure is in the connection between the symbolic and analytical parts of the process know-how, and the whole operation results in a corrective programme. An important feature of this operation is that the controller may or may not put his decision into effect at the time of diagnosis of failure or when new instructions are reaching him about desirable changes. He may wait for a correct time to act – this is a planned action.

Cybernetic systems

As already mentioned, the term cybernetics is the science of control and communication. The applied aspects of this science related to almost every field of human activity, viz. behavioural sciences, engineering, natural sciences. Cybernetics involves three concepts, closed-loop feedback, handling of information for these systems and exclusion of 'noise' (causal disturbances from the information channel).

1. *Closed-loop feedback.* It is evident from Chapter 2 that feedback loops are necessary features of systems designed to seek their own goals; some will react to external stimulation, others will tend to follow predetermined paths and deal with any deviations as they arise. An example of such systems is a self-regulating thermostat in a central heating system, or the human conditional reflex system. In the latter, parts of the human body react automatically and swiftly to external stimulation. Another pertinent example is that of the animal homeo-

static system, with its ability to adapt itself to the environment;
this involves a tendency towards a stable organisation, hence
the term 'homeostat' from homeostatis used by some physiolo-
gists to denote stability of function or equilibrium. Thus an
animal will behave in such a way as to hold a number of essential variables, e.g. internal temperature, composition of blood,
water in tissue, etc., at values which are more or less strictly
determined. In the words of the great physiologist Pavlov:
'The animal responds to modifications of the environment in
such a way that its reaction is directed towards its own survival. As it is a physical system of definite form and extent,
it can continue to exist only as long as it is in a constant state
of equilibrium with the forces external to it.' Ross Ashby
devised a model (Ashby, 1952), which he called a 'homeostat',
that made a random search to find a stable position and then
maintained it despite changes in conditions. In all these
systems, the core of the arrangement is closed-loop feedback.
It is necessary to observe, however, that the response to the
external stimulus must be rapid both in animate and inanimate
systems. Apart from the desirability of an immediate response
to environmental changes because of a danger of breakdown,
the occurrence of a delay within a closed-loop may cause the
system to oscillate about the desired state of equilibrium
without coming to rest. This is particularly serious if the process involves a large amplification (Bode, 1945), i.e. when a
small input signal brings about a large driving power.

2. *Signals and information.* Information is an essential part
of cybernetics. This work is associated with Wiener (loc. cit.),
Shannon (Shannon & Weaver, 1949), and has its origins in
Gibbs' statistical mechanics. Shannon was the first to pro-
pound the idea of information as a quantity that can be
measured in physical terms. He showed that there was a
maximum rate at which information can be communicated
without error through a physical channel of specified bandwidth and signal-to-noise ratio. Furthermore, information
may be shown to be inverient to transformations of the waveforms by which it is conveyed, i.e. transformations are of the
'coding' of information type. Finally, the information (I)

conveyed by a group of signals may be expressed by the sum (Σ)

$$I = -\sum_{k=1}^{n} p_k \log p_k \qquad (3.1)$$

where n is a finite number of different signals of which the kth occurs with a relative frequency or probability p_k; the quality 'finite' must be emphasised, since otherwise the information cannot be measured. Cybernetics is merely concerned with the handling of this information by control systems and not with its conveyance.

3. *Exclusion of 'noise'.* The problem of reducing causal disturbances or noise is one of the main pillars of cybernetics. The pioneer in this field of separating the signal from the noise was Norbert Wiener, the originator of the term cybernetics in its modern context. (This term was used by André Marie Ampère (Schuh, 1965) in the late 1830s to denote social sciences in a table of human knowledge appended to his book *Essai sur la philosophie des sciences.*) Wiener showed that mathematical techniques could be used in design which would minimise noise interference (Wiener, 1933, 1949). This may lead to a design of adaptive control systems, the filtering characteristics of which alter to suit the types of signal and noise. This principle may be further extended to optimise plant performance in all kinds of industrial operations, in response to varying external conditions, such as temperature, pressure, rate of input, type of raw material, etc. Some of the systems thus developed have the ability to learn and deal with breakdowns by using alternate channels of communication and actual operation. Indeed, machines can be made which exhibit behaviour resembling that of conditioned reflexes in animals (Uttley, 1956). Other examples of such adaptive systems are the *machina speculatrix* (Grey Walter, 1950), a type of an electric tortoise, and its more sophisticated version (Deutsch, 1955), which can learn to tread a simple maze. A recently developed learning machine in the U.S.A., comprising 'artificial neurons' or 'artrons', can remember and solve problems; it responds to punishment and rewards by

learning desired behaviour and capitalising on its own mistakes, and it is capable of making decisions and searching for better solutions. Moreover, if some of the network is destroyed, the system is able to find another route and accomplish its objective. In fact, this machine is being developed by the U.S. Air Force to deal with unexpected conditions encountered in high-performance aircraft and satellites. Other adaptive machines have already been discussed in Chapter 1 (perceptrons, etc.).

But returning to the problem of noise and its relation to information, it is obvious that the noise reduces the gain in information transmitted, i.e. noise impairs the content of information and its intelligibility. However, we must not draw rash conclusions therefrom that, since all transmitted information tends to lose something during its transmission due to noise, therefore in the end a system will emerge in which information is no longer possible. In fact, some cyberneticians attempted to apply this spurious reasoning to human society by maintaining that since communication tends to degrade itself, therefore the idea of social progress (Guilbaud, 1959) is absurd. This is one of the several fatuous predictions made by over-enthusiastic cyberneticians blinded by visions of an electronic 'zoo' and endless cohorts of marching robots.

Having now discussed some aspects of communication, it is opportune to turn to the other part of cybernetics, namely the problem of control. This will be discussed, first of all, in connection with objectives and types of automatic control, with special emphasis on optimisation; this will be followed by a review of the means of control.

OBJECTIVES AND TYPES OF AUTOMATIC CONTROL

The last decade has witnessed the start of a revolution in the design of control systems. Until about five years ago automatic control in industry was concerned with individual control systems, each relating to a single variable, e.g. the steam-engine governor controlling the flow of steam into a turbine. In industrial plants there was a large number of these single-purpose control systems, one unrelated to the other and each situated in a different place. Even the location of all these systems in a central control room and the supervision of the instrument dials by a small group of technicians did not affect this arrangement of a multitude of single-purpose units that used analogue techniques with separate equipment for each control function.

Supervisory computer control

A break with this outlook occurred with the introduction of integrated control systems, the object being to produce products of a given quality using the minimum raw materials and energy. In the early 1960s the advent of reliable and fast digital computers made this possible. At the beginning, the computer was used to supply the operator with information obtained as a result of the digestion of input signals from various parts of the plant. Then the computer took over some of the functions of the operator by arranging for automatic changes of the operating conditions directly through conventional analogue control equipment – this is known as 'supervisory computer control'.

Direct digital control

A more advanced stage in plant control (Stainthorp, 1966) is 'direct digital control', in which the computer completely controls the operation by reading the instruments and then directly operating motors, relays and control valves on the plant. The control equipment here is totally integrated. Computer programs can then be devised to optimise conditions and cope with various contingencies. This technique has already been applied in a number of large plants, and digital computer control is now seriously considered for almost all new process plant of significant size in the chemical and metallurgical and electrical and nuclear power supply industries. Even the giant radio telescope at Joddrell Bank in Cheshire is controlled by this method.

The success of this technique of control is based on the development of highly reliable, relatively inexpensive and extremely fast miniaturised computers. Some of these computers, though fast and complex, are so small that they fit a medium-size suitcase, consume only the same power as a 100-watt electric bulb and can work under extreme conditions of temperature, humidity, etc. Hence these 'micro-computers' may be used to control small processes and may be installed in aircraft, space vehicles and missiles, where space is at a premium. The range of applications is further increased by the use of cathode-ray displays to show not only alpha-numeric characters but also graphs and diagrams.

The 'brain' of the direct digital control (D.D.C.) system is the computer proper, which goes through a program of instructions that are stored as a sequence of machine orders.

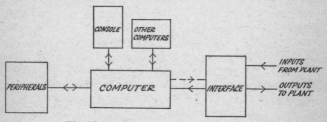

Fig. 27. *D.D.C. system.*

In a large plant hundreds of continuous signals reach this computer, which is capable of manipulating digital numbers at speeds reckoned in an addition or multiplication per microsecond. The link between the signals and the machine is via an interface (Fig. 27), which contains a number of components, such as scanner-to-sample signals at a rate appropriate to the computer speed, an analogue-to-digital converter and amplification devices. In D.D.C. systems in chemical plants the scanner examines inputs from certain points on flow control loops at a rather slow rate, viz. one per second, or even minute. The sequence of sampling is not always fixed, since abnormal readings may induce the scanner to examine various points at a much higher rate. The time intervals between successive scans are used by the computer to carry out enormous numbers of calculations in order to obtain optimum conditions and to issue instructions in a digitised form; these instructions are then changed by an analogue-digital converter into analogue signals which are sent to electro-pneumatic controls on valves.

The peripheral equipment includes several different pieces of equipment, e.g. means of inserting the operating program, a logging typewriter to obtain a permanent record of plan operation, visual display of plant conditions, tape-card readers and alarm printers. In addition, the operator must retain ultimate control via the input and output stages in case of computer failure and also to bring the plant on stream. It must be noted that the basic program is stored in a locked-out store, which is not accessible to the console operator; this program can only be altered as a deliberate act of policy.

The problem of reliability is, of course, of supreme importance. The machines now available for direct digital control can be guaranteed to fail less than about twice a year; this is less than the failure rate of other components of the plant itself. However, the speed with which the failures can be rectified is also of importance. This criterion is known as 'availability', its complement being termed 'down time'. At present availabilities of 99·5% are obtainable, though it is hoped to obtain availabilities of 99·95% in the near future, i.e. down times may amount to only four hours per annum! To match this superior reliability, a sound power supply must be available, i.e. one without surges, dropped cycles or spikes, while cases of complete power-supply failure must be catered for by banks of accumulators and provision of alternative sources of power.

The safety chain of the system must be reinforced by continuously monitoring the performance of the computer itself, passing reference signals and examining the output signals and independent alarm systems. In order to cater for departures from stability of closed-loop systems (see Chapter 2, section on stability), a stand-by analogue system must be available to enable the human operator to cope with emergencies – it is he who is the final link in the safety chain.

So far, over 90 'on-line' computer control systems have

been installed in the United Kingdom at a cost of over £6 million; total expenditure in this field is expected to rise to £15 million in 1970. The U.S.A. has made even greater progress in this direction. The cost of installing this system, the replacement of existing plant and availability of expert personnel are of fundamental importance.

As far as cost is concerned, this can be split into expenditure on hardware and software, the latter including systems analysis. It is fairly easy to assess the cost of hardware. But a similar exercise on software is in the realm of speculation. Some calculations (Stainthorp, loc. cit.) show that at a certain size of a plant the D.D.C. system is competitive with conventional systems which have three times as many measurement points. For example, the computer with its peripheral and interface equipment would cost (1964 prices) about £55 000 for a plant with 100 measurement points (40 flow, 36 temperature, 10 level, 10 pressure and 4 composition) used to operate 60 control valves. As a straight replacement of a conventional system, the D.D.C. arrangement would compete with an installation with 300 measurement points and 180 valves, owing to saving on controllers, researchers, control panels and rooms required to house large control panels. On the debit side, one has to place the considerable effort required to analyse a control system and to obtain an error-free operating program. The generation of software is a considerable part of the expense of installation. It is found, for instance, that one man-year would be required to put a program into operation for the above plant with its 100 measurement points.

This brings in the problem of trained personnel, particularly systems analysts. In large plants, teams of engineers and computer experts are essential for the economic functioning of the D.D.C. system. Better still, the plant engineers ought to acquire the knowledge of methods of computer control and relevant plant design and be able to investigate models simulating the behaviour of various systems. In this field, institutions of higher education have to play a vital part, and facilities already exist for training experts. Thus, in the United Kingdom the Loughborough Technological University and the Manchester University Institute of Science and Technology have developed computer courses for chemical engineers for the purpose of training them in the application of D.D.C. systems to chemical plant operation.

Two important possibilities may be envisaged: one is concerned with the optimisation of operation, including adaptive control, even in systems in which there are some non-linearities and random disturbances; the other with a radically different approach to the problem of 'plant-computer'. In brief, it is believed that it may be far more profitable to design a plant around a computer than to replace a control system in an existing plant by D.D.C. At present, however, the control of existing plants is replaced by a computer. Hence the production line must be flexible and sufficiently versatile to adjust itself to the demands of the controlling computer. This difficulty, plus the large expenditure on new equipment and other technical and manpower problems, hindered the uses of 'on-line' computer systems and confined them to metallurgical and chemical industries.

In the United Kingdom major investigations are proceeding at the Warren Spring Laboratory, Stevenage, into the problems and viability of controlling chemical processes. This is being done by studying the behaviour of a pilot plant, producing acetone from isopropanol, which provides a dynamic test bed for examining full-scale instrumentation and control problems and helps to generate new chemical engineering practices in plant designing; the test plant is connected via D.D.C. to a computer. One of the aspects studied is the behaviour of the system involving very fast, nearly explosive, chemical reactions; this is important, since many chemical processes are carried out well below their peak efficiency for the sake of stability and safety. Thus it may be possible to design plants of very high efficiency because of operating at nearly explosive rates of chemical reactions. In general, one of the main objectives of this study is the development of means for optimisation of plant operation.

OPTIMISATION OF OPERATIONS

The object of this exercise is to design the best systems from
among various alternatives. This may be accomplished by
studying the characteristics of various processes considered,
determining the criteria by which alternatives are to be judged
best and then selecting the best performance for the criteria
thus laid down. It is important to lay down suitable criteria,
since different optimum conditions may be selected, depending
on the type of factor chosen; the optimum, for example, for a
criterion of quantity may be different from that judged by a
criterion of quality. The effort on selecting the right criteria
that are generally acceptable is considerable. The proper
choice of such criteria may affect the effectiveness of the whole
system.

Allied to this concept of criteria, or judgement factors,
there is that of constraints; this is defined as a limit which
exists in one feature that prevents one from obtaining a better
value of another. For instance, if one insists on a minimum
time for the performance of an operation, then the question
may arise as to limits of tolerance of cost or reliability of
equipment. Constraints fall down into two classes: hard
constraints, or limits that cannot be exceeded without failure
of the systems; soft constraints, which can be treated more
leniently. It is obvious that the presence of constraints may
sometimes make it impossible to obtain best solutions.

There are other considerations that may apply when
choosing the best of several alternatives:

1. Reasoning applied to the choice of the best from well-
defined and well-known alternatives is generally different from
that obtaining in the case of ill-defined and abstruse alternatives.

2. In some cases the choice has to be made on a continuous
basis (on-line optimisation), in others at one particular instant
of time.

3. The choice of an optimum will be affected by the environmental conditions of the process and by the nature of the
process itself. The procedure applied, for example, to the

optimisation of a process with fixed characteristics is evidently different from that in which the process characteristics change.

4. The procedure will also depend on whether it is possible to obtain the optimum solution as a part of the initial design procedure (off-line) without any flexibility in the control of the process, or whether a form of adaptive control could be used in order to optimise the solution during the process.

In order to deal with this difficult and complex situation, a number of methods have been developed and are being used more extensively. Various mathematical techniques have been applied to system optimisation problems; these include (Franke, Gordon & Clymer, 1963) dynamic and linear programming, differential calculus, Pontryagin's maximum principle, calculus of variation, statistical and gradient methods.

An attempt will be made here to discuss these methods, using a bare minimum of mathematics.

OPTIMISATION METHODS

In general, there is no optimum method for performing optimisation, except in a few specific cases where the problem has a specific optimum that can be physically realised and when the details of the problem are extremely well known. The choice of methods depends on a number of factors, viz. whether or not the process will be done by man or machine.

1. *Method of search*

This is the least sophisticated method of all, and it involves a search of a set of inputs for the best output. The method applies to poorly defined systems, i.e. those for which process characteristics are not known or for which they change in time in an unknown manner. The work may, of course, be enormous in some circumstances, hence an attempt is usually made to reduce the number by applying the rules of the well-known Radio and Television game of 'Twenty Questions'. In some cases the set of inputs has a certain structure, so that

only certain points are studied, usually by means of mathematical equipment. This technique is tedious and does not
always give the optimum; the results of the search are generally influenced by laws of chance owing to the lack of data.

2. *Differential calculus*

This method employs partial differential equations to find the
optimum. Thus, if the relations between input and output
quantities are known and there are no additional constraints
on the optimum, the dependent variables can be differentiated
with respect to each of the independent variables to obtain the
optimum solution in the usual manner by equating the first
derivative to zero.

This method has certain disadvantages. Firstly, it is difficult
to apply when there are discrete changes from one size of
equipment to another or one operating condition to another.
Secondly, iterative methods must be used when the differential
equations are non-linear (i.e. with variable coefficients) and it
is difficult to identify the optimum. However, this method is
very helpful when only simple approximations to real problems are necessary or when design ('off-line') optimisation is
desirable.

3. *Calculus of variations*

This type of calculus (the Euler–Lagrange calculus) deals with
the analytical solutions of complex functions, subject to
constraints, and not with maxima or minima of functions
(Norton, 1965).

The method is most difficult, hence it is seldom applied.
Digital-computer methods have been used to carry out
enormous amounts of calculations and find by trial and error
the best approximation to the optimum required.

4. *Statistical methods*

There are two main classes of methods: classical statistics and
stochastics. Both apply when the process involved is not well
defined, so that there is some degree of uncertainty.

The first method is used when the available data are such that there is little or no time dependence from one datum point to the next, i.e. each datum is not correlated in time with the next. The idea is to select an optimum function from a given class of functions and fit a function to given data by the least-square curve fitting, multiple regression, harmonic analysis or by other techniques. Another approach is to select the best form of function with which to try to fit the data.

Stochastics (from the Greek word meaning 'he who guesses') * involve cases in which a certain element of time dependency of data at one instant of time is combined with that at neighbouring instants of time. This method is used to find optimum linear systems with respect to criteria involving communication, signal/noise problems, best control, etc.

5. *Linear programming*

In the context of linear programming, linear means that both the system and constraints are linear, while programming refers to an orderly method of solution, as opposed to trial-and-error and unorganised search methods. A system is linear when it can be represented by linear differential equations with constant coefficients. The objective here is to obtain a set of input values such as to produce the best output for a linear system having linear constraints. The term 'program' in this method must not be confused with the term computer program, though a digital computer may be used to embody such a linear program.

Various techniques exist for solving problems in linear programming. Both digital (Charnes, Cooper & Henderson, 1953) and analogue (Pyne, 1956) computers may be used in this connection; the former carries out a large number of approximations to find the maximum value of the linear function representing the objective. Linear programming can

* A stochastic process is a series of terms for which no term can be calculated in advance, e.g. daily quotations on the Stock Exchange. This unpredictability does not, however, imply absence of order. Stochastic processes are subject to stringent laws (Schuh, 1965).

only be applied to well-defined processes that are essentially static in nature. It is mainly used in conjunction with the allocation of resources, yielding the best solution from many alternatives.

It may be noted that non-linear programming can also be done by using digital or analogue computers. In engineering, very few systems are strictly linear, though they may behave linearly under some conditions. There are systems which cannot be regarded as even approximately linear, e.g. on–off control systems in which the magnitude of the correction is independent of that of the error and which are extensively used as temperature-control systems incorporating simple thermostats. This departure from non-linearity becomes more pronounced with an increased demand for better performance (De Barr, 1962; Norton, loc. cit. pp. 17, 48 and 50).

6. *Dynamic programming*

This has been defined (Bellman, 1957; Leitmann, 1962) as 'the mathematical theory of multi-stage decision processes'. In this method a sequence of decisions must be made in a defined order, so that criteria must be established by which an optimum sequence of choices must be determined, hence the term multi-stage. These decisions must constitute an optimal policy with the state resulting from the first decision, whatever the initial state is. It is clear that time plays an important part because of the sequence of decisions, and both deterministic and stochastic techniques may be used in arriving at an optimum policy. Since the dynamic programming calculations are discrete in nature and involve numerical methods, it is advantageous to use digital computers for obtaining the maximum.

Dynamic programming deals with finding the optimum solutions in situations where there are one or more elements of dynamics present; the systems studied are linear and non-linear. An example of such a problem is aircraft landing, where the error at the final stage is of *vital* importance. While the control of the aeroplane during the last mile before touchdown may be decisive in establishing the landing conditions, the downward velocity and position at touchdown are of fundamental importance; here the present control variable and value of reference have to be extrapolated to their future values and their future error determined, and the method of control is responsive and adaptive to the actual performance of the system. Another example is of selecting the least-expensive route of proceeding from an initial to a final point via a complex network; here decisions are required at each point or node of the network. In all these cases involving dynamic programming, Bellman's principle of optimality applies, viz. 'an optimal policy has the property that whatever the initial state and the initial decisions are, the remaining decisions must constitute an optimal policy with regard to the state resulting from the first decision'.

7. Pontryagin's maximum principle

This method is in many ways related to Bellman's optimality principle, and it is subject to the same limitations as the calculus of variations (Rozender, 1959a; Pontryagin *et al.*, 1962). It was first introduced (Pontryagin *et al.*, 1956, 1960; Rozender, 1959b) in 1956, and may be used to establish certain properties with a minimum of mathematical manipulation. However, the principle itself cannot be stated without recourse to advanced mathematical expressions. Suffice it to say that Pontryagin's maximum principle is concerned with systems which can be described by a number of first-order partial differential equations derived by means of dynamic programming; the actual maximisation of the set of partial differential equations is achieved by maximising a much simpler relation, known as a Hamiltonian function. It should be added that the Pontryagin principle does not provide any direct technique for synthesising the optimal control. An example of an application of this principle is the specifying of the optimal (minimal feed) thrust program for a vertical flight of a rocket *in vacuo* in a uniform gravitational field (Meditch, 1964), e.g. in a lunar hovering mission. A preliminary design may be obtained for the system from the application of the principle.

8. *Gradient methods*

These methods (Brooks, 1959; Chestnut *et al.*, 1963) are termed 'hill-climbing' or 'step descent', terms which are used in order to show that the object is to find the highest or lowest point on a hypersurface (contour map), as shown in Fig. 28. The sought function or objective function is represented by a hill having arbitrary contours; constraints form curved boundaries on the hill and define the region within

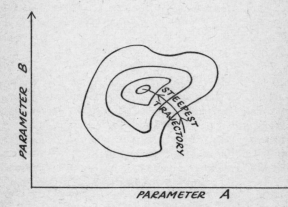

Fig. 28. *Gradient method (steepest descent).*

which the variables may be adjusted. Gradient methods afford a set of continuous control law leading to an optimum solution. The calculations are carried out by means of digital computers, which by means of programs known as 'optimisers' alternately assess slopes in different directions to find the path of the steepest descent.

While digital computers are of importance in solving problems in which there is a large but finite number of allowable points, though forming a smooth envelope, analogue computers are used in cases involving continuous computation without a finite number of allowable points. In the latter, the solution-seeking point moves in the steepest direction, as before, but is able to follow temporarily a less-steep direction because of a constraint in the system. In essence, the idea is to construct a hypersurface, as before, by making it represent errors of equation fitting; the solution sought is then a minimum. Finally, there are also techniques (Brunner, 1961) involving alternate continuous analogue computation and digital decision-making; the analogue part is concerned with the dynamic simulation; the digital part then deals with the steep-descent problem. The important consideration is to minimise the error, which may be reduced by a systematic search or random sampling. Gradients are particularly useful in optimising non-linear systems, either alone or in conjunction with statistical methods (Chestnut *et al.*, 1962). They are useful because they lend themselves to preliminary hand calculations which yield an approximate value of the optimum south; this is followed by easily programmed computer operations to obtain an accurate value of the optimum.

Summing up the review of the optimisation methods, it is clear that these are of some complexity and involve the use of computers. The applications of these methods (Franke, *et al.*, loc. cit.) cover a wide technological spectrum ranging from space travel, via chemical and engineering operations, to human factors. Table 7 shows some of the applications of these methods. It may be seen that the optimisation methods may be applied to many different types of problems in static and dynamic systems, which in turn may be linear or non-linear. In most cases, the optimisation exercise has deep and far-reaching practical implications, since considerable cost, human effort and computer time are involved. Indeed, schemes already exist to optimise the optimisation exercise itself! In all this, it is essential to have not only trained systems analysts with considerable engineering and mathematical background but also personnel with sufficient vision and initiative to use the available techniques and automatic controllers now in existence.

Table 7. *Applications of optimisation methods.*

Technological areas*	Methods used	Applications	Remarks
Chemical	Dynamic programming; gradient; calculus of variation	Chemical process control; heat exchange; half-lives in a radio-chemical mixture; chemical kinetics	Chemical industry is one of the leaders in exploiting optimisation methods
Computer	Gradient; others to a lesser extent	Optimisation of computer hardware and software, e.g. best wiring layout for minimum wire lengths; fitting of algebraic equations to given discrete data or a given function, or differential equations to continuous data – both a form of optimisation; tracking of transfer functions; simulation of models	Possibility of automating curve- and surface-fitting
Electrical	Gradient; dynamic programming	Design of electrical circuits and components; optimal and electrical transformers and optimal thermal design of transistors; optimal use of steam and hydro sources for electrical power	Design of special noise filters, based on Wiener's work; missile guidance; hunting a missile; detection of patterns

TABLE 7.—*continued.*

Technological areas*	Methods used	Applications	Remarks
Human	Gradient; dynamic programming; others	Optimisation of pilot environment in aircraft; optimisation of training of technicians and operators; tracking of moving targets by humans	Possible economic and medical uses
Mechanical	Linear and dynamic programming; variational calculus; gradient; others	Structural design for minimum cost or weight; surveying; choice of sets of thermal or nuclear radiation layers; adjustment of radar antennas; rheology of materials; design of fire-control equipment	Considerable range of mechanical engineering applications
Operational research	Dynamic programming; others (all involving P.E.R.T. or C.P.A. techniques)	Highway construction; oil drilling; assembly lines in a large-scale production; production and inventory control program; business forecasting; optimal maintenance; transport problems; assignment of labour to jobs under various conditions	Generally the object is the optimum utilisation of resources

TABLE 7.—*continued.*

Technolo- gical areas*	Methods used	Applications	Remarks
Space travel	Calculus of variations; gradient	Self-optimising system for flight control; structural design of space vehicles for various conditions; navigation in space; optimisation of orbits, rendezvous strategies, etc.	Scientific and military uses

* Technological areas given in alphabetical order.

CONTROLLERS

A controller accepts and operates on the error signal to produce an output that is capable of altering the input to the plant in order to produce a desired condition, i.e. to reduce the error to an acceptable value in the shortest possible time consistent with stable operation. In general, the controller output must be supplied at a high power level relative to the error signal, hence a feature of controllers is power amplification.

The simplest and most widely used type of controller is that involving a proportional relation between its output and error, the proportionality constant being termed 'gain of the controller'. This gain may be adjusted to various values. In the on–off controller the gain is infinite, since the range of output is biased to occur entirely in one direction with zero output for one sign of error. In other cases, however, the gain has limited values; for all positive values of error the full controller output occurs in one direction, while for all negative values the full correction is in the opposite direction.

A serious limitation of the proportional controller is that it is unable to change its output if the error is zero. Hence an error must always be present in the controller to correct a disturbance in the system. This is overcome by using a proportional-plus-integral type of controller, which is capable of providing a correction even in the absence of an error.

A more sophisticated type of controller is possible, since the above cannot deal with the often-encountered situation that there is a time lag between the time of detection of an error and the time any influence of the proportional controller is felt by the controlled quantity. In fact, what is needed is a device which would enable the controller to anticipate the error and take steps to offset it before it actually occurs. To achieve this object, an element is added to the controller, which is a fraction of the rate of change of error; this type is known as the proportional-plus-derivative controller.

The three types of controller may be combined in certain situations to form a proportional-plus-integral-plus-derivative controlling device, though some compromises are necessary owing to physical limitations, such as friction hysteresis, stiffness, etc. On the other hand, current research is concerned with the development of self-optimising or self-adaptive systems, which change their characteristics in order to maintain optimum performance when the conditions of operation of the plant itself alter. These systems are capable of dealing with information collected on a continuous or sampling basis, and also with random inputs and non-linear elements. In this complex field both digital and analogue computers are playing an important part.

Whatever the complexity of the above devices, information about plant inputs and outputs must be carried to the controller without distortion or undue delay, sometimes over long distances through various obstacles. This is achieved by various types of transmission links, which carry the signals by electrical, hydraulic, pneumatic, mechanical or human agencies. There is an increasing tendency to remove man from the measuring transmission and controller elements in order to do the job more economically and efficiently, while eliminating subjective errors of judgement.

The transmission links pass the signal from the measuring instruments of the plant to the controller. One may consider these instruments to be part of the controller, though operating at some distance from it. These measuring means must have a speed of response which is fast relative to the speed of the plant. Moreover, they must not alter the behaviour of the plant or load it and create a disturbance. Furthermore, the measurements must have an inherent accuracy consistent with the desired plant output. In other words, the error in the controlled quantity, which actuates the controller, must be equal to the difference between the desired value of plant output and that of the actual output.

Another difficulty is that the signal may become contaminated with background noise, hence the necessity to process it in order to recover the message before use. The 'information theory', which deals with this and other relevant matters, is playing a vital part in this field.

The most widely used transmission link is electrical, since the costs of installation and maintenance are relatively low, the transmission speed is high and the ease of processing electrical messages is appreciable. On the other hand, converters or transducers must be used in order to convert signal into an electrical form, since few signals originate as such. For instance, a flow rate or pressure must be changed into a voltage or current to transmit the signal, and then be reconverted into a mechanical form for use by the controller.

In the case of pneumatic transmission it is also necessary to use converters at both ends, but these are simple and reliable. However, air-operated control systems are less flexible and more difficult to install than electrical links. They are mainly used in instances where the length of the link is short and the time for data transmission is small compared to the required speed of response of the whole system. Somewhat similar considerations apply to the hydraulic link, while mechanical transmission by gears and linkages is efficient provided the plant and controller are parts of an integral compact unit. It is, of course, essential to design the overall system with due consideration being given to each part. This analysis of the system and its consequent synthesis forms the background of discipline of systems engineering.

Automatic controllers

Automatic control is concerned with correcting disturbances (external actions) and maintaining or altering conditions in a process without the direct participation of man. The instruments used for this purpose are termed 'automatic controllers'; they act upon the control element, which is part of the controlled equipment or object, to produce an effect in the latter – the factor that is subject to control being known as the controlled parameter or quantity. The controller acts on the control element in the light of information received

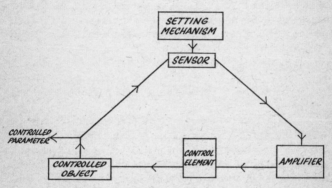

Fig. 29. *Automatic control* (*indirect action*).

from a measuring instrument known as a sensor, which measures the difference between the controlled parameter and the desired value for a given process; the controller also contains a means for setting up the desired value of the controlled parameter, i.e. a setting mechanism. Fig. 29 shows the interaction between the various parts of an automatic controller. The only additional item is the amplifier, which may or may not be included. For instance, no amplifier is included when the sensor can develop enough force to actuate the control element in order to eliminate the departure of the controlled parameter from the desired value or error, this type of controller being termed 'controller of direct action'. In controllers of indirect action, however, the signal from the sensor has to be amplified by pneumatic, hydraulic, electronic or other means, to actuate the control element; this ancillary equipment is known as the regulating unit of the controller. The stability, speed of response and adequate performance are further improved by incorporating various additional units, known as stabilising units; these include delay devices, internal feedbacks, etc.

Controllers may also be divided into two main classes on the basis of their response to a disturbance: astatic and static types. The former is concerned with controllers, which restore, in the event of a disturbance, the controlled parameter to its desired value independently of the magnitude of the disturbance; the static type refers to controllers which may set up a new value of the controlled parameter that differs little from the desired value, but the new value depends on the size of the residual disturbance. Static controllers are, in general, more stable and more reliable because of their relative simplicity.

As regards the process equipment which is controlled by the above means, there are single and multiple systems. In single systems each variable is controlled by its own controller independently of other variables and controllers, so that the controllers act independently of one another. In multiple systems, on the other hand, the control process of each controller controls not one but several or all of the control elements, so that a deviation in one of the controlled variables will cause a deviation in the others, the controllers interfering with each other. It should be noted, however, that some of these interferences may be reduced or completely eliminated by external coupling between the controllers. A brief description of some types of control systems will now follow.

Types of control systems

The following control systems will be considered (Aizerman, 1963): astatic and static direct action, astatic and static of indirect action, multiple, oscillators, discontinuous action, extremal and special controllers (Table 8).

Table 8. *Controllers with discontinuous and continuous action.*

Main types	Position of equilibrium	Action	Example
Discontinuous (periodical)	Without	Periodic oscillation	Systems with an interrupter key actuated by a cam driven by an electric motor
Continuous	Without	Oscillatory	Thermostatic heating system
	With	Direct; static	Centrifugal governor
		Direct; astatic	Piston pressure controller
		Indirect; static	Automatic speed control for electrical machines
		Indirect; astatic	Above – with feedback units
		Indirect; with derivative action	Above – with a stabilising transformer
		Multiple	Coupled controller

Direct action. Controllers using direct action are most widely used because of their simplicity and reliability. They include conical, plane, float level, electric and other controllers. In conical controllers the control element consists of small metallic balls held down by a spring between the plane and conical plates. When the centrifugal force changes, there results a change in the distance between the centre of the ball and the axis of revolution. A typical example of this type of controller is the centrifugal governor * (Fig. 30). An axial force is produced in this steam-engine by the rotation of masses *W*. As the speed of the engine increases and approaches the desired value, this axial force exceeds that caused by the initial compression of the spring *S*, and the valve begins to close. If no load is present, equilibrium will be attained when the valve is completely closed. In practice, however, a valve opening will be required to maintain a given speed, and the

* A sketch of this governor is also shown in Fig. 3.

equilibrium condition for a given initial compression of S that represents the desired speed will vary with load.

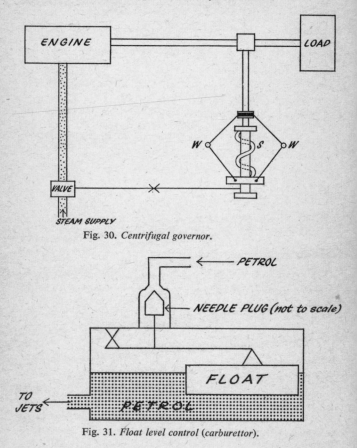

Fig. 30. *Centrifugal governor.*

Fig. 31. *Float level control* (carburettor).

In plane controllers, weights move in the plane of revolution, so that two forces act on the weights: a centrifugal force of inertia, which depends on the angular velocity of the axis, and a tangential force of inertia, which is proportional to angular acceleration (the controlled parameter here is the angular velocity). Hence this is a direct-action controller with derivative action – the latter being due to the tangential force (acceleration is the first derivative of velocity).

Another type of controller is the float-level variety, e.g. in water reservoirs or car carburettors (Fig. 31) the level of the liquid actuates a device for opening or closing a valve to admit sufficient fluid in order to attain a given level. The floating-ball device in a lavatory cistern is an example of this type of controller. In all the above controllers there occurs a static error, since various valves of the controlled parameter are related to various loads on the control equipment.

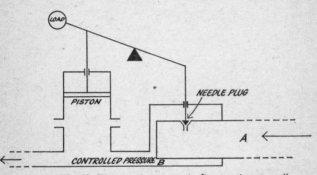

Fig. 32. *Piston pressure astatic direct action controller.*

An example of an astatic direct-action controller is one involving piston pressure, the piston being loaded by a weight and not by a spring (Fig. 32). As the pressure in the system rises, the piston moves and raises the load so that the needle plug reduces the intake of the fluid from A to B, and vice versa. Here equilibrium is only possible for a given value of pressure, so that only this value of pressure can be obtained for any equilibrium position of the control element. These astatic controllers, though versatile and effective, usually require additional devices for stabilisation, such as hydraulic dampers.

In general, an important drawback of all direct-action controllers is the need for large moving masses or loads to

obtain the necessary movement. Since large forces increase
friction, sensitivity is reduced as well as stability. Hence it is
advantageous to incorporate an amplifier to supply the
necessary energy for translatory movement; an indirect action
controller then results.

Indirect action controller. These fall into two classes: astatic
and static.

The astatic controller may incorporate a hydraulic, pneumatic or electric amplifier between the control element and

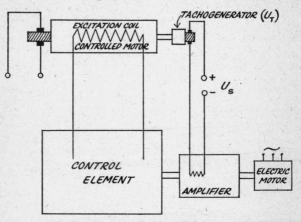

Fig. 33. *Automatic speed control of an electrical machine*
(astatic control, indirect action).

sensor. Fig. 33 shows an automatic speed-control system for
an electrical machine. The tachogenerator is the sensor which
supplies information about the speed of the machine (controlled parameter), while the desired machine velocity is
characterised by a standard electrical potential U_S. The difference between the tachogenerator potential U_T and U_S is fed
into an amplidyne, whose output is connected to a regulating
motor, which in turn alters the resistance in the excitation
coil of the controlled electric motor, so that its speed is
changed, until U_S and U_T are equal; the system is then at
equilibrium. The control element in this arrangement consists
of a regulating motor, intermediate gears and a rheostat. The

amplifier, which is interposed between the sensor and control element, consists of an amplidyne and an electric motor.

Indirect action static controller. While in astatic controllers the position of the sensor pointer determines the displacement

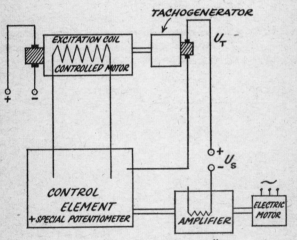

Fig. 34. *Indirect action static controller.*

velocity of the control element but not its position, in static controllers the reverse is true, i.e. to each position of the pointer there corresponds a definite position of the control element. Consider, for example, the automatic speed control of an electrical machine, as in Fig. 33, but with a feedback arrangement in the control element (Fig. 34). Here the control element contains in addition to the components shown in the preceeding figure, a potentiometric device connected in such a way as to enable the amplifier to receive a feedback signal from the control element as well as the error signal ($U_S - U_T$) from the tachogenerator. Hence the position of the controlling unit of the amplifier depends not only on the sensor but also on the deflection in the regulating unit of the control elements. However, the improvement of control has to be paid partly

by introducing a residual deviation (static error) in the controlled parameter. The reason for this additional error is that
a steady or equilibrium state can only be attained if there is a
difference between the actual and desired speeds, when the
difference ($U_S - U_T$) balances the potential of the feedback
signal.

The static error introduced by the above system may be
removed by using 'floating' instead of the 'rigid' feedback, as
above. Here the feedback can only act during the control
process and disappears when the system is near its equilibrium.

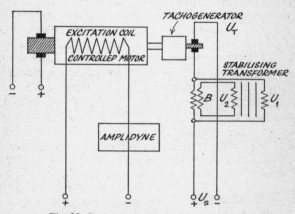

Fig. 35. *Derivative action* (*indirect action controller*).

Thus the floating feedback system partakes of the advantages
of both the astatic and static controllers: during the operation
the controller behaves as a static device, but the value of the
controlled parameter returns to the same value, depending on
how much of the feedback effect is removed. These floating
feedbacks may be hydraulic, pneumatic and electrical.

An effective way of stabilising indirect action controllers
consists of using the principle of derivative action. These
devices may assume different forms. For example, in an
electrical system derivative action is obtained by means of a
differentiating circuit. Fig. 35 shows a system of automatic

control of the speed of the electrical motor, using derivative action; the latter is obtained by means of a stabilising transformer. The potential U_1 which is proportional to the difference (error signal) between the standard potential (U_S), corresponding to the desired speed, and the tachogenerator indication of the actual speed U_T, is applied to the primary coil of the transformer; the potential U_2 of the secondary coil of the transformer, which is proportional to the rate of change (derivative) of U_1, is applied to the coil (B) of the amplidyne. Hence the control action is proportional to both the error signal (deviation of speed) and its derivative.

Multiple control. This type refers to systems in which the control process for any one parameter is not independent of the others; here controllers may interfere with one another, and the control process of each controller may control several of the control elements. In some cases, this interference is reduced or eliminated by external couplings between the controllers, so that an error in one of the parameters does not cause a deviation in others.

Oscillatory controllers. This type is concerned with systems where there is no equilibrium position. In these systems the control element can only be set in two fixed positions (on/off) or moved with one of two fixed speeds (full forward/full backward), i.e. oscillatory controllers are of the two-position type. These controllers cannot move the control elements unless there is a change in the sign of the deviation between the desired and actual values of the controlled parameters. As a result, the controlled parameter oscillates about the desired value.

An example of this type of controller is the thermostatic system shown in Fig. 36. The heater is completely switched on when the mercury column in the thermometer opens the contacts; the heater is completely switched off when the column closes the contacts. It is not possible to set up the required temperature value when the heater is completely on or off; an intermediate degree of heating is thus required. As a result, the temperature oscillates about the required value, and the mercury column in the thermometer oscillates about the contact plates so that it switches alternately on and off. Also, the time during which the heater is on or off

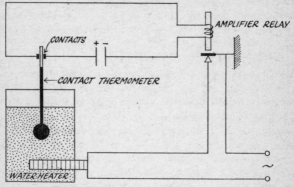

Fig. 36. *Oscillatory controller.*

changes with changes in the maintained temperature. The corrective action in this system is either zero or has some fixed value, while its behaviour is, in general, non-linear. The

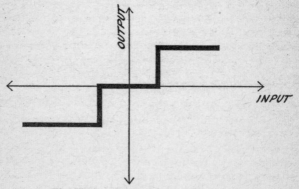

Fig. 37. *On–off system.*

general form of the characteristic of an oscillatory (on–off) system is shown in Fig. 37. The behaviour of such a system under different conditions is as follows:

1. Under normal conditions the controlled parameter oscillates at constant amplitude about its mean value; the period of oscillation is increased by increased delay between the initiation of a controlling signal and its effect on the controlled parameter. The delay itself may be caused by inertia, thermal capacity of load, etc.

2. When the load on the system is increased, then there will be a response more marked in one direction than another, so that the mean value of the controlled parameter will differ from the desired value; this is also known as droop or offset.

3. If the load remains constant but the sensitivity is increased by augmenting the magnitude of the controlling action, then the natural frequency of oscillators is increased.

4. If the inertia of the system is increased, then both the period and amplitude of oscillation are increased.

This type of 'on–off' control has some advantages over linear control, since in the former the full controlling action is always available to make the output coincide with the input, particularly when the input is in the form of a large step-function; in a linear system this is not so, since the controlling action decreases as the error decreases. There is a difficulty, however, in the possibility of an overshoot, so that it is desirable to add a damping signal proportional to output velocity. Therefore, a simple damped on–off system, which is non-linear, can in many respects give a better performance than a linear system.

Periodically discontinuous action controllers. In these devices elements do not act continuously on the other hand, so that an action circuit opens or closes, for instance, in a manner independent of the behaviour of the process. For example, an interrupter or key may be inserted into the sensor circuit. If this key is actuated periodically by a cam driven by an electric motor, then the controlled parameter is not measured continuously but only when the key is closed. It is only then that the sensor signal acts on the control element. The key may be replaced by a more complex mechanism, but the general behaviour of the system is the same. There is no action during the

time when the key or its equivalent are not depressed, while
during the time intervals when the key is closed, the controller
is active and behaves like a continuous controller. These controllers must not be confused with 'on–off' controllers, as in
some textbooks.

Discontinuous controllers are preferable in some instances
to their continuous partners. Firstly, the controller is dis-
connected from the object for a large part of time, so that one
controller can be used for several parameters in turn. Secondly,
they perform better than continuous controllers in systems
involving operations with large delays. Thirdly, they have
several technical advantages, particularly in production
automation.

Extremal controllers. The term 'extremum' refers to the
existence of a maximum or minimum of the controlled parameter. An extremal controller continuously 'searches' for the
position of the control element giving the maximum or minimum value of the controlled parameter, while only that
parameter is measured. These controllers can be used in two
ways in automation production. (*a*) When the controlled parameter can be measured directly, then this value is fed directly
into the extremal controller. (*b*) When the parameter cannot
be measured directly but has to be calculated from measurements of other factors, e.g. the specific rate of fuel flow, then it
is necessary to transmit first those measurements into a computing device and feed the result, i.e. the value of the controlled parameter, into the controller. This type of controller
makes it possible also to construct more sophisticated controlling devices in cases when several controlled parameters
are involved.

Various techniques may be used to construct extremal controllers. The simplest involves a differentiating unit by means
of which it is possible to obtain the value of the first derivative
of the function of the position (p) of the control element, i.e.
the value of the controlled parameter (y), i.e. $y = f(x)$;
suitable relays and regulating motors can then be inserted to
function at the maximum or minimum of y. A major dis-
advantage of this type of controller is its sensitivity to noise,

since a number of small bogus extrema appear in the presence of noise. However, the system may be improved to deal with these complications. Although extremal controllers are little used at present, it is believed that their advantages will tilt the balance towards more extensive application in automation.

Special controllers. This type includes universal, individual and specialised controllers. Universal controllers are capable of controlling a wide variety of parameters and systems; they usually consist of a universal unit plus points for fitting special sensors and regulating units according to usage. Even less specialised devices are now available in automation production, known as aggregate systems, which consist of separate units, a kind of building block, each unit dealing with one operation on a signal, e.g. differentiation; various controllers can thus be assembled to form complex controllers.

Individual controllers are quite different from the above. They usually form an integral part of a machine, e.g. jet engines. Allied to these are specialised controllers which are designed to control a given parameter in a number of machines (objects), e.g. indirect-action pressure controllers and nearly all direct-action controllers.

It must be stressed that in all these considerations a knowledge of control theory is of fundamental importance. This theory enables one to design controllers, to predict and thus to deal with operational difficulties, to adjust controllers and to run the process efficiently. Some major difficulties experienced in automated processes are due to the neglect of the control theory in industrial operations. Powerful mathematical methods for solving differential equations, Laplace and Fourier transforms, stochastic analysis, digital and analogue computers, and optimising techniques are essential for the proper use of control in automation processes.

EPILOGUE

The stage is now set for the creation of automata and automated systems with their brains (computers), arms (controllers), connections (feedback loops), sensors and actuators, and working modes. The master sorcerer, having accomplished the feat of creating Wiener's Golem (Wiener, 1964), is about to depart, leaving the stage of history to his apprentice, who will press the switch to activate the cybernated systems and extend man's dominion over nature. The consequences of these actions are discussed in another volume of this series (Rose, 1967), which considers the effects of automation in the industrial, commercial, economic, social and other spheres, and also endeavours to offer predictions, if not hope, for the future.

REFERENCES

AIZERMAN, M. A. 1963. *Theory of automatic control*. Pergamon Press, Oxford.
ASHBY, W. R. 1952. *Design for a brain*. Chapman & Hall, London.
BELLMAN, R. 1957. *Dynamic programming*. Princeton Univ. Press, N.J.
BODE, H. W. 1945. *Network analysis and feedback amplifier design*. Van Nostrand, New York.
BROOKS, S. H. 1959. In *Ops Res.*, **7**, 430–457.
BRUNNER, W. 1961. In *Proc. west. jt Computer Cong.*, May.
CHARNES, A., COOPER, W. W., and HENDERSON, A. 1953. *An introduction to linear programming*. Wiley, New York.
CHESTNUT, H., *et al.* 1962. Third J.A.C.C., New York.
CHESTNUT, H., *et al.* 1963. *Automatic optimisation of a poorly defined process, Part II*. Fourth J.A.C.C., Minn.
DE BARR, A. E. 1962. *Automatic control*, pp. 83–93. Chapman & Hall, London.
DEUTSCH, J. A. 1955. In *Discovery*, **16**, 515.
FRANKE, W. C., GORDON, B. B., and CLYMER, A. B. 1963. In *Instrums Control Syst.*, February, 127–130.
GUILBAUD, G. T. 1959. *What is cybernetics?* Heinemann, London.
LEITMANN, G. (ed.) 1962. *Optimisation techniques*. Academic Press, New York.
MEDITCH, J. S. 1964. In LEONDES, C. T. (ed.) *Advances in control systems*, Vol. I., pp. 66–73. Academic Press, New York.
NORTON, A. R. M. 1965. *Introduction to variational methods in control engineering*. Pergamon Press, Oxford.
PONTRYAGIN, L. S., *et al.* 1956. In *Dokl. Akad. Nauk SSSR*, **110**, 7–10.
PONTRYAGIN, L. S., *et al.* 1960. *Izv. Akad. Nauk SSSR*, **24**, 3–42.
PONTRYAGIN, L. S., *et al.* 1962. In NEUSTADT, L. (ed.). *The mathematical theory of optimal processes*. Interscience, New York.
PYNE, I. B. 1956. In *Trans. Communs Electronics*, 139–143.

Rose, J. 1967. *Automation: its uses and consequences* (C.S.P. 9). Oliver & Boyd, Edinburgh.

Rozender, L. I. 1959a. In *Automatika i Telemekhanika*, **20**, Nos. 10–12.

Rozender, L. I. 1959b. In *Automn remote Control*, **20**, 1288, 1405, 1517.

Schuh, J. F. 1965. *Principles of automation*, p. 307. Philips Technical Library, Eindhoven, Holland.

Shannon, C., and Weaver, W. 1949. *The mathematical theory of communication*. Univ. of Illinois Press, Urbana, Ill.

Stainthorp, F. P. 1966. In *Chem. Engr*, March, 33–36.

Uttley, A. M. 1956. Conditional probability machines and conditioned reflexes. In *Automata Studies*. Princeton Univ. Press, N.J.

Walter, W. G. 1950. In *Discovery*, **11**, 90.

Wiener, N. 1933. *The Fourier integral and certain of its applications*. Cambridge Univ. Press, London.

Wiener, N. 1948. *Cybernetics*. Wiley, New York.

Wiener, N. 1949. *The extrapolation, interpolation and smoothing of stationary time series with engineering applications*. Wiley, New York.

Wiener, N. 1964. *God and Golem, Inc.* Chapman & Hall, London.

BIBLIOGRAPHY

Barbe, E. G. 1967. *Linear control systems*. Inter. Textbook Co. Scranton, Pa.

Bell, D. A. 1962. *Intelligent machines*. Pitman, London.

Bellman, R., and Kalaba, R. 1964. *Mathematical trends in control theory*. (A selection of classical papers by Nyquist, Maxwell, Bellman, Pontryagin, Minorsky, Bode *et al.*) Dover, New York.

Bowden, B. V. 1953. *Faster than thought*. Pitman, London.

Chestnut, H. 1965. *Systems engineering tools*. Wiley, New York.

Harrison, H. L. and Bollinger, J. G. 1963. *Introduction to automatic controls*. Inter. Textbook Co., Scranton, Pa.

Lloyd, S. O. 1962. In *Automation*, June, 86–90; July 84–90.

Raven, F. H. 1961. *Automatic control engineering*. McGraw-Hill, New York.

Rosie, A. M. 1966. *Information and communication theory*. Blackie, London.

Glossary of Terms

Access: The process of obtaining data from or placing data in storage.

Access time: Time required to read out or write in data from a data storage system.

Actuator: A device to convert energy of fluids into mechanical motion (in an electrical actuator the rotary motion of an electric motor is converted into linear motion).

Adaptive control system: A control system which continuously adapts itself to changing environmental conditions by monitoring its own behaviour and optimising its parameters.

Address: A label, name or number identifying the location where data are stored.

Algorithm: A fixed step-by-step procedure for solving problems.

Amplidyne: A special d.c. generator used as a high-response rotary power amplifier in conjunction with servomechanisms.

Amplifier: A device for increasing the magnitude of an input quantity by a known ratio.

Amplitude: Magnitude of a variable, usually the peak value, without regard to variation with time.

Analogue: Representation of numerical quantities by means of physical variables, e.g. voltage.

Analogue computer: A computer which represents variables by physical analogies. While a digital computer is said to count, an analogue computer measures.

A.P.T.: Automatically Programmed Tools – a system for programming the numerical control of machine tools by means of an English-like computer language.

Arithmetic unit: Part of a computer in which arithmetical and logical operations are performed.

Assembler: A computer program that operates on symbolic input data to produce from such data machine instructions, item for item.

Automatic control: A device which is capable of correcting deviations of a system from a standard state.

Automatic programming: A technique for digital computers in which the logical circuits of the computer itself are utilised in programming and coding the problem.

Automation: The theory, art or technique of making processes self-acting; in other words, operation by means of feedback control without human intervention.

Bandwidth: A property of a control system describing the limits of sinusoidal input frequencies to which it will respond.

Binary: A system in which combinations of only two digits represent any number or quantity of units, i.e. a number representation system with a base of two.

Decimal code	Binary code
0	0000
1	0001
2	0010
3	0011
4	0100
5	0101
6	0110
7	0111
8	1000
9	1001
10	1010

Bit: A coined word from *bi*nary digi*t*; this is one of the whole numbers, 0 or 1, in a single position, in the binary scale of notation.

Block: A symbol for a group of components performing a specific function; a group of blocks, representing the function of a control system or machine, is termed a block diagram.

Bode plot: A logarithmic plot of frequency versus gain or phase of a servomechanism, or of the transfer function of one of its elements.

Boolean algebra: A system of symbolic logic that uses the same logical rules of operation as binary algebra, which uses only the numbers 0 and 1.

Byte: A generic term to indicate a measurable portion of consecutive binary digits, e.g. a six-bit byte; it may also designate a group of binary digits usually handled as a unit.

Central processor: A part of a computer exclusive of input, output, auxiliary storage and peripheral devices.

Character: An electrical magnetic or mechanical profile used to represent a letter or number.

Character set: An agreed set of characters from which selections are made to denote data; the total number of a set is fixed, e.g. a 48-character set may contain the 26 letters of the alphabet, 10 numerals and 12 special characters.

Characteristic equation: A differential equation of a linear system when the applied forcing function is made equal to zero.

Code: A system of symbols and the method for using them to represent rules for processing information, e.g. a computer or machine code represents the operations built into the hardware of a computer.

Compatibility: The ability of a computer to process data prepared on another computer.

Compiler: A routine, i.e. set of coded instructions in proper sequence, for a digital computer, which produces a specific program for a particular problem by automatic means.

Controlled variable: A quantity which is directly acted upon by a control system.

Controller: A device which measures the value of variable quantity or condition and which then operates to correct or limit the error, the latter being the difference between the measured quantity and a specified reference.

Core storage: The main or internal memory of a computer; it is usually expressed in terms of k (1000), e.g. a 10k machine has 10 000 characters of core storage.

Critical damping: A condition which has just sufficient damping to prevent any overshoot in response to a step function command.

Cybernetics: The study of control and communication in man and the machine (Wiener).

Cycle time: The time required to complete the process of reading and restoring information in a magnetic core memory; synonymous with memory cycle.

Damping: A means of absorbing energy in an oscillatory system so as to prevent large and destructive overshoots or continual oscillation.

Data logger: A device which centrally records physical processes and events in sequence.

Data storage: A device which accepts and retains units of information and which will produce them, unaltered, on command.

Debug: To remove all malfunctions or mistakes from a device.

Decibel: A unit used to express the ratio between two specified values of power [$dB = 10 \log_{10} (P_1/P_2)$], where P_1 and P_2 are the two values. (A power gain of 100% is about +3 dB.)

Delay relay: A relay, i.e. a device for receiving and retransmitting a signal in a reconstituted form along a more favourable path, which is designed for a time delay.

Density: The number of elements stored per unit of dimension, e.g. 100 b.p.i. denotes 100 bits stored per inch of magnetic tape.

Derivative response: An automatic controller mode of operation in which there is a continuous linear relation between the rate of change of the controlled variable and the position of the final control elements.

Detroit automation: 'Automatic' transfer of a workpiece between different single-purpose machines or between different parts of the same machines.

Digital computer: A computer which solves problems by operating on discrete symbols of integral value, performing arithmetic or logical processes (in an analogue computer data are manipulated by measurement).

Digitise: To render a continuous or analogue representation of a variable into a discrete or digital form.

Eccles-Jordan: A bistable device, i.e. one that has two stable states, which assumes a given stable state depending on the history of the inputs. Also known as a flip-flop device.

Electrostatic storage: Special cathode-ray tubes capable of storing binary data.

Equivalent binary digits: The number of binary digits required to express a number of another base with the same precision. For example, over three times the number of decimal digits is required to express a decimal number in binary form.

Error: The difference between the instantaneous value of the controlled variable and the desired value or set point. Synonymous with deviation.

Feed: Time during which work is done on a work-piece in an automatic machine tool cycle.

Feedback: A means of automatic control in which the actual state of a process is measured and used to obtain a quantity that modifies the input in order to initiate the activity of the control system.

Feedback transducer: A component of a feedback control system which converts the output to a related signal.

Flip-flop: A device capable of assuming two stable states.

Fourier analysis: The analysis of complex waveforms into sinusoids consisting of the fundamental frequency of the waveform and its harmonics.

Gain: The numerical value of the amplification factor associated with the input/output ratio of a system.

Gain margin: The quantity by which the magnitude of the open-loop transfer function of a closed-loop system is less than unity at phase crossover, i.e. where the phase angle of the transfer function is 180°.

Game theory: A mathematical process of selecting an optimum strategy to face an opponent with his own strategy.

Gang punch: A process for duplicating cards and card data.

General-purpose computer: A computer designed to operate on a program of instruction for many types of data-processing problems rather than being designed to fulfil a single function.

Gigacycle: One thousand million cycles per second (G/s).

Grid: In optical character recognition (OCR), two mutually orthogonal set of parallel lines used for measuring character images.

Hardware: The electrical, electronic, magnetic and mechanical devices or components of a computer.

Heuristic: Trial-and-error method of tackling a problem, as opposed to the algorithmic approach.

Hybrid computer: A computer which has a combination of digital and analogue features.

Hysteresis: The lagging in the response of a unit of a system behind an increase or a decrease in the strength of a signal.

I.D.P.: Integrated Data Processing, i.e. processing of data by a system in which all procedures are tied to a computer.

Imaginary number: The product of a real number and the operator j, which is equal to $\sqrt{-1}$; a complex number is the sum of a pure real and a pure imaginary number.

Impedance: The steady-state resistance to a single-frequency alternating-current flow in an electrical circuit containing capacitance, resistance and inductance.

Information retrieval: A branch of computer sciences relating to the techniques for storing and searching large or specific quantities of information.

Information system: The network of all communication methods within an organisation.

Information theory: The mathematical theory concerned with channels, rates of transfer, noise, etc., relating to information.

Input: Information which a control system's elements receive from outside.

Instability: A condition of a feedback control system in which large sustained oscillations of the controlled variable occur, so that the latter is no longer controlled by input instructions.

Instruction: A coded program step that tells the computer what to do for a single operation in a program.

Intelligence: The developed capability of a device to perform functions that are normally associated with human intelligence, such as learning or reasoning.

Intelligence (artificial): The study of computer and related techniques to supplement the intellectual capabilities of man.

Interface: The point of contact between different systems or parts of the same system; it may involve codes, speeds, sizes and formats.

k: Symbol for 1000 (kilo-).

kB: A symbol used to designate 1000 bytes per second.

kC: Symbol used to designate 1000 characters per second.

kD: Symbol used to designate 1000 digits per second.

Language: A defined set of characters which is used to form symbols, and the rules for combining these into meaningful communications.

Language (machine): Information recorded in a form that may be made available to a computer.

Linear programming: A branch of operational research involving mathematical techniques for solving optimisation problems, the relevant equations being linear.

Linearity: The property of a control element which will permit its output to be represented by a straight-line function of its output.

Machine language: Information recorded in a form directly understood by the computer.

Magnetic core: A data storage device based on the use of a highly magnetic, low-loss material, capable of assuming two or more discrete states of magnetisation.

Magnetic drum: A data storage device using magnetised spots on a magnetic rotating drum; permits quasi-random medium-speed access to any part of its surface.

Magnetic tape: A device for storing digital or analogue data in the form of magnetised areas on a tape of plastic coated with magnetic iron oxide.

Margin of stability: The extent to which a linear feedback system quantitatively meets one of the conditions for stability, e.g. Routh's or Nyquist's criteria.

Microsecond: One-millionth of a second (μs).

Millisecond: One-thousandth of a second (ms).

Modular: The ability to increase a system in small steps (modules).

Nanosecond: One thousand-millionth of a second (ns).

Numerical control: A means of controlling machine tools through servomechanisms and control circuitry, so that the motions of the tool will respond to digital coded instructions on tape.

Nyquist diagram: A closed polar plot on the complex plane of the open-loop transfer function of a closed-loop (i.e. feedback) control system.

Offset: A sustained error due to an inherent characteristic of positioning controller action (synonymous with droop or drift).

On-line operation: A type of operation in which the input of information is fed directly from the sensors to the computer.

Open-loop control: A control system in which there is no feedback.

Operational amplifier: A high-gain amplifier with feedback – the basic element of an analogue computer.

Output: Information which a control system transmits as a result of its input.

Parallel: Simultaneous processing of the individual parts of a whole, such as bits on characters.

Parameter: A variable corresponding to a given condition; an arbitrary constant as distinguished from a fixed constant.

Peripheral equipment: Ancillary devices under the control of the central processor, e.g. magnetic tape units, printers or card readers.

Phase margin: The angle by which the phase of the loop ratio of a stable system differs from 180° at unity gain of the loop ratio; it is a measure of the degree of stability of a feedback control system.

Plotter: A visual display device in which a variable is graphed by an automatically controlled stylus.

Plug-board: A panel, containing a matrix of interconnected unit connectors, capable of storing a program or storing data.

Program: A set of coded instructions to direct a computer to perform a desired operation or solve a predefined problem.

Program tape: A magnetic or punched paper tape which contains the sequence of instructions required for solving a problem on a digital computer and coded in language which may be read by the computer.

Punched card: Thin cards on which digits are represented by holes in selected locations for storing data.

Punched tape: A paper or plastic tape in which holes are punched to serve as a digital storage device.

Radix: Base of a number system, e.g. in the binary system using symbols 0 and 1 the binary numbers are of radix 2, while in the decimal system it is 10.

Random access: Access to data storage in which the position from which information is to be obtained is not dependent on the location of the previous information, e.g. as on magnetic drums or cores.

Real number: The set of all rational and irrational numbers.

Real time: Pertaining to actual time during which a physical process occurs; a method of processing data so fast that there is virtually no time interval between enquiry and result, or the performance of a computation during the actual time that the related physical process occurs.

Root locus: A plot of the characteristic equation in the complex plane of showing the effect of changes in parameters of a feedback control system on its stability.

Routh's criterion: A method of determining the stability of a linear system without actually solving for the magnitude of the roots of the characteristic equation. (Also known as the Routh-Hurwitz criterion.)

Routine: A set of coded instructions arranged in proper sequence to direct a digital computer to perform a desired series of operations.

Sensor: A device which senses a physical event, e.g. sound or light.

Servomechanism: A feedback control system designed to maintain the state of the controlled variable, usually position, proportional to the input.

Signal: The event, electrical quantity or phenomenon that conveys information from one point to another.

Sinusoid: Variation in a quantity proportional to the trigonometric sine or cosine function.

Software: General-purpose programs used to extend the capabilities of computers, including compilers, assemblers, monitors, executive routines, etc.

Stability: The condition of a dynamic or feedback system in which the controlled variable always corresponds to the input.

Step function: A sharp change in state of a signal.

Symbolic logic: The representation of rules of normal logic by mathematical or special symbols.

System: An assembly of components united by some form of regulated interaction to form an organised whole. Also a collation of operations and procedures, men and machines by which an industrial or business activity is carried on. In the realm of computers a system is defined as an organisation of hardware, software and people for co-operative operation to complete a set of tasks for desired purposes.

System A.D.P.: An automating programming software system that includes a programming language and a number of machine-language programs.

Systems analysis: The organised step-by-step study of the detailed procedure for collection, manipulation and evaluation of data about an organisation, for the purpose of determining what must be accomplished and the best method of accomplishing it in order to improve control of a system.

Tabulator: A data-processing machine which reads information from a storage medium and prints totals and data on paper.

Throughput: Term used to designate the productivity of a computer, based on all aspects of an operation.

Time sharing: The use of a device for multiple purposes during the same time interval.

Transducer: A device for converting some physical property of a process into a measurable quantity; this term is more limited than a sensor.

Transfer function: The ratio of output to input expressed in a mathematical form.

Transform: An algebraic expression or operator which permits a mathematical relation to be changed into a form that lends itself better to solution of problems, e.g. the Heaviside operator $p = (\mathrm{d}/\mathrm{d}t)$ converts a differential equation into a polynomial in p. Other examples are Fourier and Laplace transforms.

Word: A set of characters or bits which is handled by the computer circuits as a unit; word lengths are fixed or variable, depending on the computer.

Index

Numbers printed in **bold** *type refer to a more detailed treatment; entries under Glossary are not included here.*

*Other titles in this series
from Oliver and Boyd
are described on the following pages*

AUTOMATION: ITS USES AND CONSEQUENCES

John Rose

Although advanced industrial societies are already committed to automation, where machines and processes are controlled by computer instead of by man, effective planning for automation on a large scale demands a more widespread knowledge of the likely consequences than there is at present.

Dr Rose considers automation in relation to its uses and describes its mode of operation in industry, commerce, public administration, banking and so on. This points already to some of the economic, labour, management, and social problems of automation with which the author deals in turn. Truly, automation affects people in every place of employment, not only on the workshop floor but also in the boardroom. New skills have to be acquired and greater mental dexterity must be developed. This is precisely the problem of automation, because 'one of the greatest pains of human nature is the pain of a new idea'.

The reader wishing to learn more about the scientific ideas behind automation may turn to CSP 8, also by Dr Rose, entitled *Automation: its anatomy and physiology.*

John Rose is Principal of the College of Technology and Design in Blackburn. With his essay on *The problem of technological barriers* he won first prize in the 1966 international competition organised by Shell Chemicals Ltd and the British Association of the Advancement of Science. He is especially interested in computer science education.

CSP 10

CHEMICAL EXCHANGES IN MAN: A PHYSIOLOGICAL ESSAY

Bryan F. Matthews

Chemical exchanges are a necessary part of life processes. The chief function of the lung, for example, is to provide the cells of the body with oxygen and to remove their carbon dioxide waste. In man this is accomplished by making use of two systems: one supplying air, the other blood. With the aid of haemoglobin, the circulating blood carries to and from the tissue cells large amounts of oxygen and carbon dioxide. The lungs supply the air and, acting as a gas exchanger, load the blood stream with oxygen and eliminate the carbon dioxide.

In this book Dr Matthews describes the various chemical exchanges in man and develops his theme along principles common to these exchanges wherever they take place in the human body. Beyond this description of *what* and *where*, he attempts to answer the question *how*—thus we learn about the mechanisms involved. This highlights some of the uncertainties typical of much general physiological research. The final question is *why* chemical exchanges are necessary. Throughout we are shown that controlled exchanges singly or in combination help to preserve the integrity of the human organism

Bryan F. Matthews is Lecturer in Physiology at Aberdeen University.

THE EVOLUTION OF THE GALAXIES

Vincent C. Reddish

Galaxies are vast assemblies of millions and millions of stars, tens of thousands of light-years across, millions of light-years apart. How do they change with time? This is the mainspring of the astronomer's interest in the evolution of the galaxies, from which the question arises: Was there a beginning? Is there an end? In considering these problems Dr Reddish examines the theory of origin of the galaxies.

All the information that astronomers obtain about the stars, gas clouds, and galaxies comes from analysing the radiation received from them, especially light waves. Thus the astronomer can be regarded as a collector of photons. The results of his research give the masses of the stars, their temperature and composition, their brightness and their motions. The astronomer, however, is more than a collector of photons because his theoretical interpretations of the data have built up over the years a picture of how stars condense out to diffuse interstellar clouds of hydrogen and helium; how all the other elements we know are fused from hydrogen in nuclear reactions at temperatures of tens and hundreds and thousands of millions of degrees in stellar interiors; how the elements are blown back into the gas clouds when the stars explode; and how later generations of stars form from clouds enriched with these chemical elements. One such star is our Sun.

Vincent C. Reddish is at the Royal Observatory, Edinburgh. During part of 1966 he was Visiting Foreign Professor of the American Astronomical Society, Warner and Swasey Observatory, Cleveland, Ohio.

THE BASIS OF MODERN PHYSICS

John M. Irvine

Modern physics is concerned with those branches of physics which, for their theoretical interpretations, depend upon ideas developed during the twentieth century. These ideas are necessary to explain observations made beyond the normal limits of the macroscopic world. For example, when we consider systems moving with speeds approaching that of light, we require the theory of relativity in place of our usual concepts of space and time; when we discuss the structure of the atom we need quantum theory instead of the mechanics of Newton.

In this elementary introduction to modern physics, Dr Irvine sets the stage by giving us an account of the results of classical physics—from the laws of classical mechanics to Maxwell's electromagnetic theory. He then considers Einstein's special theory of relativity, together with some of its startling predictions.

While many simple accounts of relativity are available, simple treatments of quantum theory are less common, and this has led the author to deal with the latter at greater length than is usual in books of this size. He therefore includes three chapters concerned respectively with the problem of the interaction of the electromagnetic field with matter, the old quantum theory, and modern quantum mechanics. He concludes with a collection of problems, some partially solved and some very far from solution, which face modern physicists.

John Maxwell Irvine is Lecturer in Theoretical Physics at Manchester University.

ELECTRONIC COMPUTERS

John C. Cluley

The author presents the basic information necessary for understanding what computers are and how they can be applied to the solution of problems met with in commercial data processing, factory management, engineering, and scientific studies.

The idea of using electronic techniques, either for computation or for non-numerical tasks, immediately faces one with the necessity of acquiring some basic knowledge of the nature of computers and what can be done with them. For instance, if we are concerned with design problems in engineering we may find it worthwhile to use an analogue computer—for scaling, adding, integrating, and differentiating. For work requiring high levels of accuracy we shall probably need to use a digital computer. In either case we must know something of the basic structure, the function of the various parts, the 'hardware'—beginning with the several forms of binary symbols and proceeding with a discussion of conventional circuits using diodes, resistors and transistors, etc. We need to know also about 'software' or programming facilities—beginning, for example, with an introduction to the use of machine and symbolic codes, sub-routines, loops, and modifiers.

But what of the future? Mr Cluley concludes his book with a brief look at the prospects indicated by the use of computers for non-numerical tasks such as pattern recognition and linguistic studies.

John C. Cluley is Senior Lecturer in the Department of Electronic and Electrical Engineering at Birmingham University.